CW00376530

QUIZBOOK

QUIZBOOK

CAN YOU BANK ON THE THINK TANK?

Foreword by
BILL TURNBULL

Based on a BBC Programme **BBC**

hamlyn

An Hachette UK Company
www.hachette.co.uk

First published in Great Britain in 2016 by Hamlyn,
a division of Octopus Publishing Group Ltd
Carmelite House
50 Victoria Embankment
London EC4Y 0DZ
www.octopusbooks.co.uk

Think Tank™ and © 2016 12 Yard Productions (Investments) Limited.

All rights reserved. No part of this work may be reproduced or utilized
in any form or by any means, electronic or mechanical, including
photocopying, recording or by any information storage and retrieval
system, without the prior written permission of the publisher.

ISBN 978-0-600-63468-3

A CIP catalogue record for this book is available from the
British Library.

Printed and bound in the UK.

10 9 8 7 6 5 4 3 2 1

Think Tank is produced by 12 Yard. Think Tank is a trade mark of
12 Yard Productions (Investments). All rights reserved.

BBC and the BBC logo are trademarks of the British Broadcasting
Corporation and are used under licence. BBC logo © BBC 1996.

CONTENTS

FOREWORD

BILL TURNBULL

Hello. Thanks for joining us, and welcome to our *Think Tank* book. I hope you're reading this because you're a massive fan of the programme and can't wait to get your hands on our latest offering. If so, welcome, old friend. It's great to have you along.

On the other hand, perhaps you're new to the encyclopedic wonders of the TT and have been given this as a present. In which case, may I say what an appropriate gift this is for someone as intelligent as yourself – and by the way, Happy Christmas/Birthday/Anniversary (delete as appropriate).

Or maybe you're in a bookshop, just browsing. Please, don't put me down. Buy this book. They need the business.

You might be wondering what a Think Tank is and what it does. And working with this lot, that question has crossed my mind as well from time to time. Well, the dictionary definition of a think tank is 'a research institute or other organization providing advice and ideas on national or commercial problems'.

That's what our Tankers do, more or less. OK, less. From all over Britain, and from all walks of life, they come together to offer guidance, knowledge, and sometimes the wrong answer to our three contestants. But they're all nice people and a lot of fun.

How did I get here? After 15 years on the *BBC Breakfast* sofa, and more than 20 years before that as a TV and radio reporter, I thought it was time for a change. Getting up at 3.30 in the morning is interesting once or twice, but after a couple of thousand times, the pleasure does wear off a bit. So what could be more refreshing than to host a quiz show? I'd always wondered what it would be like, and whether I would be any good at it. And then I got my chance.

My first encounter with the Think Tank was in a dark corner of a little TV studio, where we were performing what's called a 'run-through', so that I could see how it worked and the producers could see if I was up to the mark. Just three of the team were there – Jackie (a retired local government worker from Morecambe), Max (a PR executive from London) and Lucy (a dance teacher from Kent).

From the first round it all clicked, and I knew it was going to work. The format was unusual, with the Think Tank answering questions, then asking them, then answering again. The questions themselves were challenging, but not too tough; there was plenty to get your head around. Above all, we enjoyed ourselves. There's lots of room for merry banter, and no one takes it too seriously. More than anything else, the name of the game is entertainment. Well, actually, the name of the game is *Think Tank*. But you get my drift.

So I hope you enjoy this book as much as you enjoy the show itself. And if you haven't seen the programme yet, then perhaps this will be a delicious appetizer for the golden hours of TV viewing that lie ahead when you tune in.

And now, it's time to see if *you* can bank on the Think Tank.

Good luck!

HOW TO PLAY *THINK TANK*

The BBC quiz show *Think Tank* was launched in March 2016. Hosted by long-time *BBC Breakfast* anchor and *Strictly Come Dancing* contestant Bill Turnbull, the show has already become a popular fixture in the daytime schedules.

Each show features three contestants who answer general knowledge questions for a cash prize. The contestants are helped by the Think Tank, a group of eight pre-selected members of the public who appear on screen rather like a jury. The members of the Think Tank have been asked most of the questions in advance of the show and their answers are displayed or revealed to the contestants while they are considering their own answers. With expertise in many diverse areas of interest, at least one member of the Think Tank will come up with the right answer…but it's up to the contestants to choose which one that is. Each correct answer puts £200 in the pot.

In the show, there are five rounds of questions in each episode. All three contestants take part in the first three rounds, at which point the contestant with the least money is eliminated. The two remaining contestants battle it out in the fourth round. Each is asked five questions and the winner is he or she who gets the most correct answers. In the event of a draw then the competition goes to 'sudden death'. Once a victor is determined, he or she is then asked Question: Impossible, something that no one on the Think Tank was able to answer correctly. If they should get the answer right then the contestant will have £1,000 added to their prize money. If not, then they get to take home the money in the pot. Remember only the winner takes home the prize, and the unfortunate loser goes home with nothing but their pride!

How to use this book

With this book, you and your family and friends can test yourselves and each other with the general knowledge questions featured in the series, using the help of the Think Tank, of course. While the book mirrors the series in many ways, a few changes have been made to make it more interesting for those playing in the comfort of their own homes.

The book includes 30 quizzes, each one featuring four rounds. Round 1 has six questions, Round 2 has nine, while Rounds 3 and 4 have five questions each, making a grand total of 750 questions. For easy access, and to make it harder to look up the answers (which are given at the back of the book) and 'accidentally' see some other answers at the same time, the rounds are grouped together. So, all 30 Round 1s come first, followed by all 30 Round 2s etc. Whether you are playing on your own or with friends, it'll be more fun to work through the quizzes one by one rather than answering all Round 1s in a row and so on. It'll keep the questions fresh. That way, you can also keep a running total of the money you might have won had you been playing the game on the TV with Bill, and dream about what you might have spent it on!

If you are playing with friends and family you'd be best advised to sort out pens and paper, that way you can all answer the questions at the same time by writing down the answers. It might be a good idea to appoint a 'quizmaster' to ask the questions and, of course, to keep order. They could also keep a note of how much 'money' you'd be winning – remember, you get £200 each time you get an answer right, but only the winner gets to 'take home' the money.

For Round 1, you all benefit from the wisdom of the Think Tankers. Underneath each question are the eight answers they gave before the show was aired. Given their intelligence and broad knowledge of the subjects, it is certain that the right answer will be in there somewhere. Sometimes, two or even three of them even give the same answer. But that doesn't necessarily mean it's right!

For Round 2, you are on your own. No help. No conferring. There are nine general knowledge questions: some easy, some hard. Mind you, if you don't know the answer, the question's always hard. However, if you really don't know the answer, then guess, as you won't have any money taken off for a wrong answer.

Help is at hand for Round 3 because the questions have only two possible answers: A or B. Both answers are given and it's up to you to choose which one you fancy. Think hard before you decide. For a bit of fun, you could nominate two of your fellow contestants to be honorary Think Tankers and, as they do on the show, defend one of the two answers, explaining why they think it is the correct one. You can then take their advice, or not, according to your thinking.

At the end of Round 3, you could decide to eliminate those with the least 'money' in their pots, moving on to a showdown between the top two players, for example, for the last round. Otherwise, you all move on to Round 4, Question: Impossible. Take a deep breath, as this one is the hardest of all. Five fiendish questions, no help from the Think Tank, with everything at stake in a 'winner takes all' finish.

OK! That's it – you're ready to go. We really hope you enjoy the quizzes in this book. In the meantime, it might be wise to brush up on your knowledge of flags of the world, capital cities, current affairs and so on. Then you can settle down around the table and get ready to ask the fundamental question: can you bank on the Think Tank?

ROUND 1

1/1

Which TV presenter was the most commonly googled person in the UK in 2015?

CILLA BLACK	CLAUDIA WINKLEMAN	HOLLY WILLOUGHBY	JEREMY CLARKSON
BILL TURNBULL	JIM BILLS	DERMOT O'LEARY	JONATHAN ROSS

1/2

Which male tennis player won three of the four Grand Slam Singles titles in 2015?

ANDY MURRAY	RAFAEL NADAL	NOVAK DJOKOVIC	ANDY MURRAY
ANDY MURRAY	ROGER FEDERER	NOVAK DJOKOVIC	ROGER FEDERER

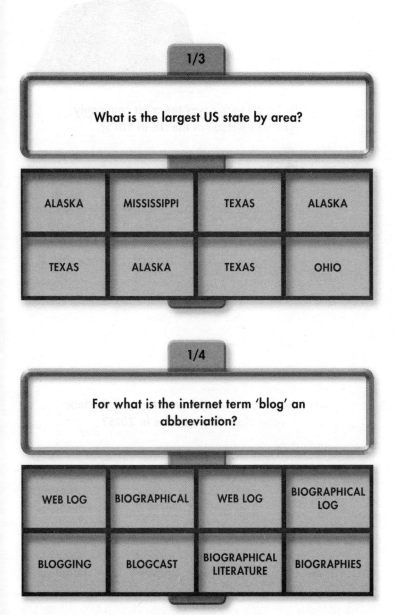

1/3

What is the largest US state by area?

ALASKA	MISSISSIPPI	TEXAS	ALASKA
TEXAS	ALASKA	TEXAS	OHIO

1/4

For what is the internet term 'blog' an abbreviation?

WEB LOG	BIOGRAPHICAL	WEB LOG	BIOGRAPHICAL LOG
BLOGGING	BLOGCAST	BIOGRAPHICAL LITERATURE	BIOGRAPHIES

QUESTIONS

15

QUESTIONS

1/5

'Zorro' is the Spanish word for which animal?

BULL	JACKAL	BULL	DONKEY
FOX	FOX	BULL	HORSE

1/6

Which woman was named *Time* magazine's Person of the Year in 2015?

CAITLYN JENNER	ANGELINA JOLIE	HILLARY CLINTON	ANGELINA JOLIE
ANGELA MERKEL	ANGELA MERKEL	ANGELA MERKEL	ANGELINA JOLIE

2/1

Who sang the opening line of the original Band Aid single?

BONO	BOB GELDOF	MIDGE URE	JOHN LAING
BOB GELDOF	PAUL YOUNG	BONO	BOB GELDOF

QUESTIONS

2/2

In the *Back to the Future* films, Marty McFly travels in time in what make of car?

FORD	DELOREAN	DELOREAN	CHRYSLER
FORD	DELOREAN	DELOREAN	FORD

QUESTIONS

2/3

What animal, with the Latin name Castor, is the national animal of Canada?

BEAR	BEAVER	BEAR	BEAR
PORCUPINE	BEAR	BEAVER	HORSE

2/4

What is the highest of the five ranks of nobility in the British system of peerage?

DUKE	DUKE	ORDER OF THE REALM	DUKE
LORD	COUNT	LORD	DUKE

2/5

The Lady in the Van is the title of a memoir and play by which writer?

ALAN BENNETT	CATHERINE STEWART	JOHN LE CARRÉ	ALAN BENNETT
MAGGIE SMITH	MAGGIE SMITH	BEATRIX POTTER	JOHN PINTER

2/6

Which band were famously said to be so loud that if they moved 'in next door, your lawn would die'?

NIRVANA	SLIPKNOT	AC/DC	MOTÖRHEAD
THE BEATLES	THE ROLLING STONES	KISS	AC/DC

QUESTIONS

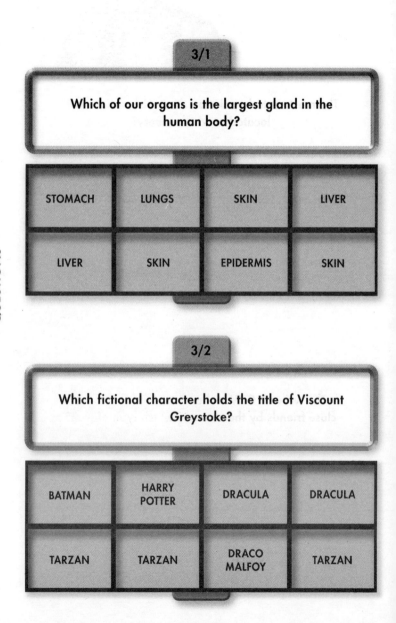

3/1

Which of our organs is the largest gland in the human body?

STOMACH	LUNGS	SKIN	LIVER
LIVER	SKIN	EPIDERMIS	SKIN

3/2

Which fictional character holds the title of Viscount Greystoke?

BATMAN	HARRY POTTER	DRACULA	DRACULA
TARZAN	TARZAN	DRACO MALFOY	TARZAN

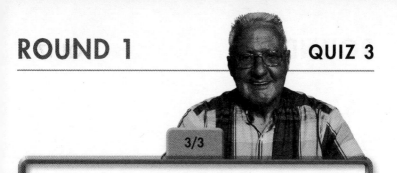

3/3

The most easterly point on the British mainland is located in which county?

DEVON	YORKSHIRE	ESSEX	KENT
SUFFOLK	KENT	KENT	ESSEX

QUESTIONS

3/4

The writer P G Wodehouse was known to his close friends by the name of which type of fruit?

APPLE	PEAR	LEMON	PLUM
PEAR	PEACH	APPLE	PLUM

QUESTIONS

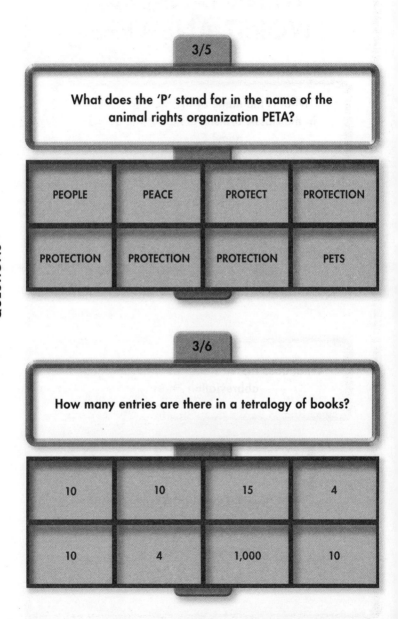

3/5

What does the 'P' stand for in the name of the animal rights organization PETA?

PEOPLE	PEACE	PROTECT	PROTECTION
PROTECTION	PROTECTION	PROTECTION	PETS

3/6

How many entries are there in a tetralogy of books?

10	10	15	4
10	4	1,000	10

THINK TANKERS' WORST ANSWERS

What is the name of the murder victim in the classic British version of the board game Cluedo?

Think Tanker:
Justin Credible

Correct Answer:
Dr Black

What does the 'A' stand for in the sporting abbreviation MMA?

Think Tanker:
Amnesia

Correct Answer:
Arts

4/1

Which pop star has a stand named after him at the football ground Vicarage Road?

ELTON JOHN	ROD STEWART	MICHAEL JACKSON	MORRISSEY
ELTON JOHN	MICHAEL JACKSON	FREDDIE MERCURY	CLIFF RICHARD

4/2

What is the name of Kim Kardashian and Kanye West's second child, born in 2015?

SAINT	JADE	NORTH	SAINT
NORTH	SAINT	SOUTH	SAINT

4/3

Heston Blumenthal's Fat Duck, once named the World's Best Restaurant, is located where?

WENSLEYDALE	BOURNEMOUTH	BRIGHTON	TEDDINGTON
ILKLEY	ST IVES	BRAY	BRIGHTON

4/4

Which sportsman announced in his autobiography *Open* that he had worn a wig for much of his career?

WAYNE ROONEY	KRISS AKABUSI	SEVE BALLESTEROS	JOHN MCENROE
SHANE WARNE	ANDRE AGASSI	JACK NICKLAUS	KELLIE / FRANK MALONEY

25

QUESTIONS

4/5

The British cartoonist Norman Thelwell was best known for his drawings of which animals?

ELEPHANTS	HORSES	DOGS	CATS
PIGS	HORSES	HORSES	DOGS

4/6

Which character has been played by Richard Attenborough, Nick Frost, Tim Allen and Paul Giamatti?

FATHER CHRISTMAS	JACK THE RIPPER	GEORGE WASHINGTON	FATHER CHRISTMAS
FATHER CHRISTMAS	FATHER CHRISTMAS	FATHER CHRISTMAS	SHERLOCK HOLMES

5/1

The title of Shaun Ryder's 2011 autobiography is *Twisting My... what?*

HAIR	MIND	NECK	ARM
HEART	TONGUE	WORDS	MELON

5/2

Who is the only singer to have had a UK no.1 single with the official theme to a *James Bond* film?

ADELE	SHIRLEY BASSEY	SAM SMITH	ADELE
SAM SMITH	SHIRLEY BASSEY	SHIRLEY BASSEY	SAM SMITH

QUESTIONS

5/3

Stephen Fry received his only Golden Globe nomination for his portrayal of which writer?

CHARLES DICKENS	D H LAWRENCE	TERRY PRATCHETT	STEPHEN HAWKING
WILBUR SMITH	OSCAR WILDE	JEFFREY BERNARD	OSCAR WILDE

5/4

Which animal takes its name from the Malay words meaning 'person of the forest'?

BEAR	ORANGUTAN	MONKEY	PANDA
ORANGUTAN	ORANGUTAN	ORANGUTAN	RACOON

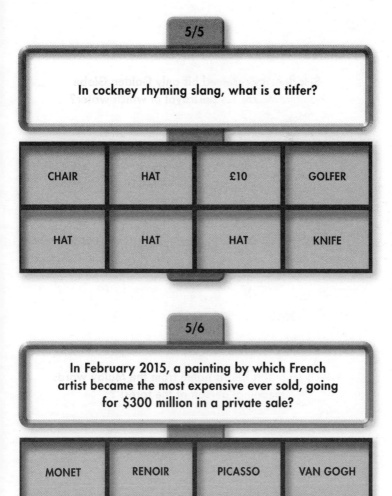

5/5

In cockney rhyming slang, what is a titfer?

| CHAIR | HAT | £10 | GOLFER |
| HAT | HAT | HAT | KNIFE |

5/6

In February 2015, a painting by which French artist became the most expensive ever sold, going for $300 million in a private sale?

| MONET | RENOIR | PICASSO | VAN GOGH |
| MANET | GAUGUIN | MONET | DALI |

QUESTIONS

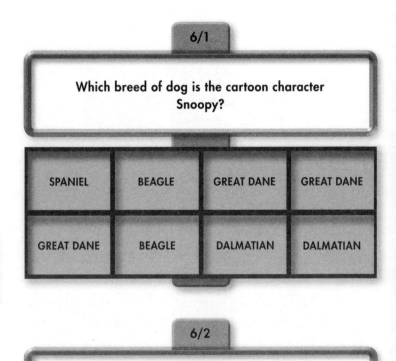

6/1

Which breed of dog is the cartoon character Snoopy?

SPANIEL	BEAGLE
GREAT DANE	GREAT DANE
GREAT DANE	BEAGLE
DALMATIAN	DALMATIAN

6/2

Before Andy Murray in 2013, who was the last British tennis player to win one of the two main Singles titles at Wimbledon?

FRED PERRY	FRED PERRY
FRED PERRY	TIM HENMAN
BJÖRN BORG	DAVID LLOYD
VIRGINIA WADE	PETE SAMPRAS

6/3

The Miracles were the backing band of which soul singer?

ARETHA FRANKLIN	SMOKEY ROBINSON
SMOKEY ROBINSON	BOB SCHNEIDER

SMOKEY ROBINSON	ARETHA FRANKLIN
STEVIE WONDER	DIANA ROSS

6/4

Barack Obama appeared in a one-off special with which British TV presenter in December 2015?

DAVID ATTENBOROUGH	BILL TURNBULL
TREVOR MCDONALD	CHRIS EVANS

BEAR GRYLLS	BEAR GRYLLS
GRAHAM GREEN	JAMES CORDEN

QUESTIONS

QUESTIONS

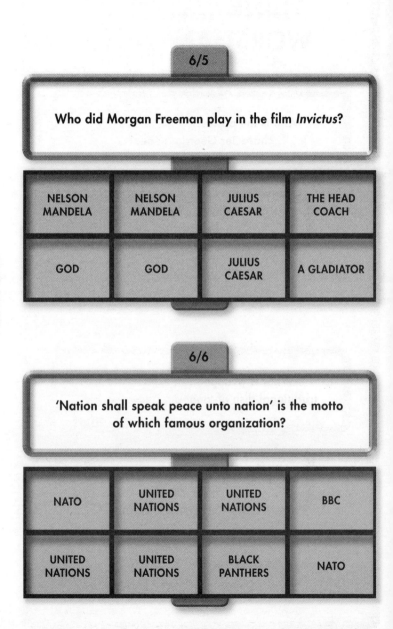

6/5

Who did Morgan Freeman play in the film *Invictus*?

NELSON MANDELA	NELSON MANDELA	JULIUS CAESAR	THE HEAD COACH
GOD	GOD	JULIUS CAESAR	A GLADIATOR

6/6

'Nation shall speak peace unto nation' is the motto of which famous organization?

NATO	UNITED NATIONS	UNITED NATIONS	BBC
UNITED NATIONS	UNITED NATIONS	BLACK PANTHERS	NATO

THINK TANKERS' WORST ANSWERS

What is the profession of the literary character George Smiley?

Think Tanker:
Dentist

Correct Answer:
Spy

What is wrapped in bacon in the traditional dish of 'angels on horseback'?

Think Tanker:
Pork chop

Correct Answer:
Oysters

QUESTIONS

7/1

How many years are there in a triennium?

3,000	3 MILLION	100,000	3
3,000	3,000	300	300

7/2

Guy Garvey has found fame as the lead singer of which Mercury Prize-winning rock band?

DAUGHTERS	METALLICA	PINK FLOYD	ELBOW
BLACK SABBATH	TRAVIS	BLACK SABBATH	AC/DC

7/3

Which everyday item is sometimes known as a bumbershoot?

| DUSTBIN | UMBRELLA | UMBRELLA | SCARF |
| BAG | BRUSH | WATCH | BAG |

7/4

According to the Internet Movie Database, who has appeared as a judge on the most episodes of the British version of *The X Factor*?

| LOUIS WALSH | SIMON COWELL | SIMON COWELL | LOUIS WALSH |
| CHERYL FERNANDEZ-VERSINI | SHARON OSBOURNE | SIMON COWELL | SIMON COWELL |

7/5

What is the English meaning of the Russian word 'spasibo'?

SPRING	SWIMMING POOL	SWIMMING POOL	BEER
THANK YOU	PARDON	SNOW	GAZEBO

7/6

Which Conservative politician was nicknamed 'Tarzan'?

MICHAEL HESELTINE	DAVID CAMERON	MICHAEL HESELTINE	ANN WIDDECOMBE
BORIS JOHNSON	DAVID HESELTINE	MICHAEL HESELTINE	BORIS JOHNSON

8/1

Who was the captain of the England rugby union team at the 2015 World Cup?

MARTIN JOHNSON	JONNY WILKINSON	CHRIS ROBSHAW	ALLAN JONES
JONATHAN	PETER SHAW	JONNY WILKINSON	JONNY WILKINSON

8/2

Knotty Ash is an area of which British city?

LIVERPOOL	BRISTOL	LIVERPOOL	YORK
BIRMINGHAM	LIVERPOOL	LONDON	BIRMINGHAM

QUESTIONS

37

8/3

The name of which soul singer was the title of a UK hit single in August 2015?

MARVIN GAYE	ARETHA FRANKLIN	ARETHA FRANKLIN	BARBRA STREISAND
BILLIE HOLIDAY	GARBRIELLE	MARVIN GAYE	STEVIE WONDER

8/4

Which writer was a new entry in the 2015 *Sunday Times* Authors' Rich List at number 4, with an estimated wealth of £75m?

STEPHEN FRY	J K ROWLING	E L JAMES	MEERA SYAL
J K ROWLING	J K ROWLING	SEBASTIAN FAULKS	J K ROWLING

8/5

The name of which British city is also the maiden name of David Cameron's wife Samantha?

WELLS	YORK	NOTTINGHAM	BATH
YORK	SHEFFIELD	KENT	BATH

8/6

The British actor Andrew Lincoln plays the role of Rick Grimes in which TV drama series?

EASTENDERS	SHERLOCK	THE WALKING DEAD	THE WALKING DEAD
THE WATCH	THE WEST WING	HOMELAND	EASTENDERS

QUESTIONS

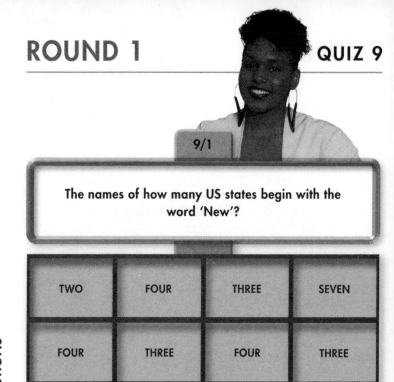

9/1

The names of how many US states begin with the word 'New'?

TWO	FOUR	THREE	SEVEN
FOUR	THREE	FOUR	THREE

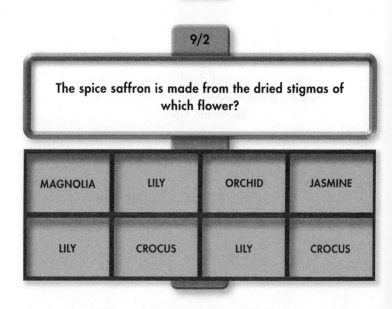

9/2

The spice saffron is made from the dried stigmas of which flower?

MAGNOLIA	LILY	ORCHID	JASMINE
LILY	CROCUS	LILY	CROCUS

9/3

Which country is known as 'The Land of the Long White Cloud'?

ENGLAND	NEW ZEALAND	TIBET	NEPAL
FINLAND	NEW ZEALAND	SOUTH AFRICA	SCANDINAVIA

QUESTIONS

9/4

Who is the central character in the books *Solo* by William Boyd and *Devil May Care* by Sebastian Faulks?

SPIDER-MAN	STEPHEN HUNT	JAMES BOND	JAMES BOND
HERCULE POIROT	HAN SOLO	SUPERMAN	SPIDER-MAN

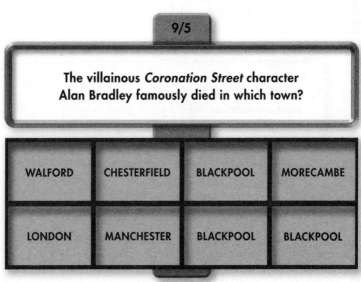

9/5

The villainous *Coronation Street* character
Alan Bradley famously died in which town?

WALFORD	CHESTERFIELD	BLACKPOOL	MORECAMBE
LONDON	MANCHESTER	BLACKPOOL	BLACKPOOL

9/6

'Double, double toil and trouble; Fire burn and
cauldron bubble.' are lines that originally appear
in which play?

WICKED	*WICKED*	*MACBETH*	*MACBETH*
HAMLET	*HAMLET*	*WITCHES*	*HOCUS POCUS*

THINK TANKERS' WORST ANSWERS

Which actor has played the title role in the most episodes of the TV show *Doctor Who*?

Think Tanker:
Matt Baker

Correct Answer:
Tom Baker

In the name of the internet abbreviation, the letters NSFW stand for 'Not Safe For...' what?

Think Tanker:
Women

Correct Answer:
Work

QUESTIONS

10/1

'Approaching Menace' is the title of the theme tune to which TV show?

MAD MEN	SILENT WITNESS	MASTERMIND	DENNIS THE MENACE
MASTERMIND	LUTHER	LITTLE BRITAIN	INSPECTOR MORSE

10/2

Which character from children's literature has 'terrible tusks and terrible claws and terrible teeth in his terrible jaws'?

THE HIPPOGRIFF	TONY THE DRAGON	THE GRUFFALO	HOOK
THE GRUFFALO	THE OGRE	DUMBO	THE GRUFFALO

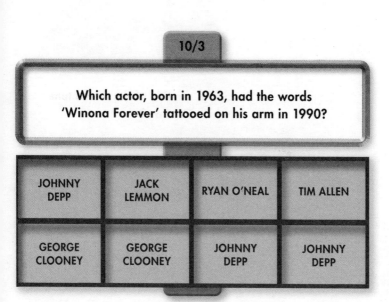

10/3

Which actor, born in 1963, had the words
'Winona Forever' tattooed on his arm in 1990?

JOHNNY DEPP	JACK LEMMON	RYAN O'NEAL	TIM ALLEN
GEORGE CLOONEY	GEORGE CLOONEY	JOHNNY DEPP	JOHNNY DEPP

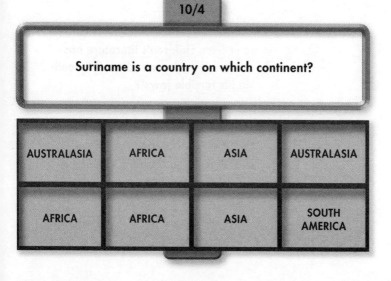

10/4

Suriname is a country on which continent?

AUSTRALASIA	AFRICA	ASIA	AUSTRALASIA
AFRICA	AFRICA	ASIA	SOUTH AMERICA

QUESTIONS

45

QUESTIONS

10/5

Who is the only US President to resign from office?

RICHARD NIXON	RICHARD NIXON	JIMMY CARTER	BILL CLINTON
RICHARD NIXON	RICHARD NIXON	RONALD REAGAN	FRANKLIN D ROOSEVELT

10/6

In Cockney rhyming slang, the word 'Gregory' refers to which part of the body?

NECK	MOUTH	HEAD	NECK
FOOT	ARM	HEAD	NOSE

11/1

What name is given to a piece of rock or metal that has fallen to the Earth's surface from outer space?

METEORITE	METEOR	ASTEROID	METEORITE
METEORITE	METEOR	METEOR	METEOR

11/2

Which film of the 1980s was set at Kellerman's holiday resort?

TRUE STORIES	STEPFORD WIVES	THE SHINING	THE SHINING
THE SHINING	DIRTY DANCING	DIRTY DANCING	ON THE BUSES

QUESTIONS

11/3

Which major US city, famous for its high rainfall, is known as 'The Emerald City' due to the lush foliage in the area?

SEATTLE	COLORADO	KANSAS CITY	SEATTLE
KANSAS	NEW YORK	NEW ORLEANS	WASHINGTON

11/4

Henry McCarty and William H Bonney are names used by which famous criminal?

AL CAPONE	ZODIAC KILLER	JACK THE RIPPER	BILLY THE KID
BONNIE AND CLYDE	BONNIE AND CLYDE	JESSE JAMES	THE BOSTON STRANGLER

11/5

What does the 'D' stand for in the name of the government agency called the DVLA?

DEPARTMENT	DRIVER	DRIVING	DRIVER
DRIVING	DRIVING	DEPARTMENT	DRIVER

QUESTIONS

11/6

What is the first name of the Queen's oldest grandchild?

ARTHUR	PETER	WILLIAM	ZARA
RICHARD	BEATRICE	ZARA	PETER

49

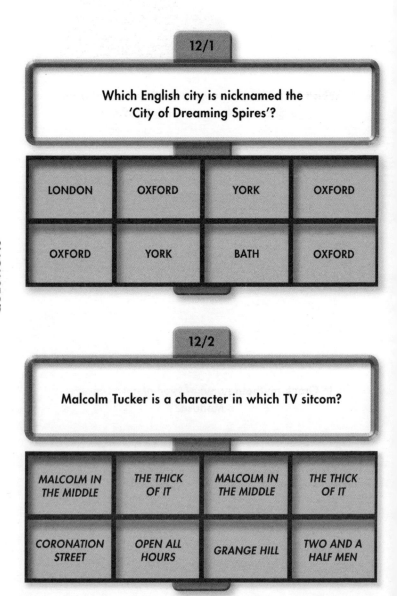

12/1

Which English city is nicknamed the 'City of Dreaming Spires'?

| LONDON | OXFORD | YORK | OXFORD |
| OXFORD | YORK | BATH | OXFORD |

12/2

Malcolm Tucker is a character in which TV sitcom?

| MALCOLM IN THE MIDDLE | THE THICK OF IT | MALCOLM IN THE MIDDLE | THE THICK OF IT |
| CORONATION STREET | OPEN ALL HOURS | GRANGE HILL | TWO AND A HALF MEN |

12/3

Which TV presenter became the Chief Scout of the Scouting Association in 2009?

CHRIS EVANS	PETER DUNCAN	BILL TURNBULL	RAY MEARS
SIMON GREEN	NICK KNOWLES	BEAR GRYLLS	BILL TURNBULL

QUESTIONS

12/4

In Greek mythology, what type of creature was Medusa?

HALF WOMAN, HALF SNAKE	GORGON	SERPENTINE	GORGON
GORGON	GORGON	SNAKE	SNAKE

QUESTIONS

12/5

Which country has been the world's largest exporter of coffee for 150 years?

COLOMBIA	COLOMBIA	COLOMBIA	COLOMBIA
BRAZIL	BRAZIL	CUBA	BRAZIL

12/6

Which former *X-Factor* contestant joined the cast of *Coronation Street* in 2015?

LEONA LEWIS	KIM SMITH	LEONA LEWIS	KYM MARSH
SHAYNE WARD	KYM MARSH	MICHELLE KEEGAN	JAMES MURPHY

THINK TANKERS' WORST ANSWERS

Which politician won his sixth Parliamentary Beard of the Year Award in 2015?

Think Tanker:
Diane Abbott

Correct Answer:
Jeremy Corbyn

What is the confectionery-inspired nickname of the football club Everton?

Think Tanker:
Quality Street

Correct Answer:
Toffees

QUESTIONS

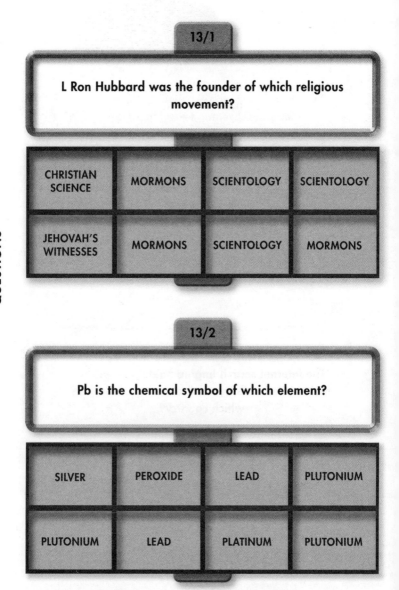

13/1

L Ron Hubbard was the founder of which religious movement?

CHRISTIAN SCIENCE	MORMONS	SCIENTOLOGY	SCIENTOLOGY
JEHOVAH'S WITNESSES	MORMONS	SCIENTOLOGY	MORMONS

13/2

Pb is the chemical symbol of which element?

SILVER	PEROXIDE	LEAD	PLUTONIUM
PLUTONIUM	LEAD	PLATINUM	PLUTONIUM

13/3

Which eccentric Oscar-winning actor has a son named Kal-El?

JIM CARREY	JIM CARREY	NICOLAS CAGE	SAMUEL L JACKSON
JACK NICHOLSON	BEN AFFLECK	ROBERT DE NIRO	MARLON BRANDO

QUESTIONS

13/4

The internet search engine Baidu, one of the most-visited websites in the world, is based in which country?

INDIA	INDIA	CHINA	CHINA
INDIA	INDIA	VIETNAM	USA

13/5

What does the 'M' stand for in the name of the
motoring abbreviation MOT?

MINISTRY	MOTOR
MINISTRY	MOTOR

MINISTRY	MOTORING
MECHANICAL	MINISTRY

13/6

'The American Tribal Love-Rock Musical' is the
subtitle of which stage musical?

ROCKY HORROR PICTURE SHOW	WE WILL ROCK YOU
ROCKY HORROR PICTURE SHOW	WE WILL ROCK YOU

WE WILL ROCK YOU	ROCKY HORROR PICTURE SHOW
ROCKY HORROR PICTURE SHOW	HAIR

14/1

The name of which dinosaur means three-horned face when translated from the Greek?

TYRANNO-SAURUS REX	TYRANNO-SAURUS REX	TRICERATOPS	TYRANNO-SAURUS
TYRANNO-SAURUS	TRICERATOPS	TRICERATOPS	TRICERATOPS

14/2

Which country did Great Britain defeat in the 2015 Davis Cup Final?

BELGIUM	GERMANY	FRANCE	CANADA
AMERICA	AMERICA	AMERICA	AMERICA

QUESTIONS

57

QUESTIONS

14/3

At the 2012 Olympics, Great Britain won a record eight gold medals in which sport?

ATHLETICS	CYCLING	CYCLING	ROWING
GYMNASTICS	CYCLING	ATHLETICS	ROWING

14/4

Which capital city takes its name from the Spanish words meaning 'good winds'?

ELDORADO	BUENOS AIRES	BUENOS AIRES	MADRID
CANCUN	BUENOS AIRES	BUENOS AIRES	MADRID

14/5

Which actor played seven different members of one family in the classic film comedy *Kind Hearts and Coronets*?

EDDIE MURPHY	ALEC GUINNESS	JIM BROADBENT	ALEC GUINNESS
EDDIE MURPHY	EDDIE MURPHY	PETER SELLERS	JERRY LEWIS

QUESTIONS

14/6

Which of the 50 US states is furthest south?

ARIZONA	HAWAII	HAWAII	HAWAII
TEXAS	HAWAII	HAWAII	TEXAS

QUESTIONS

15/1

Ready For The Weekend and *18 Months* are albums by which music producer and DJ?

PETE TONG	FATBOY SLIM	CALVIN HARRIS	ANDY LEWIS
DAVID GUETTA	DAVID GUETTA	DAVID GUETTA	FATBOY SLIM

15/2

The word 'Loiners' refers to people from which British city?

LINCOLN	LEEDS	LEEDS	SOUTHAMPTON
LONDON	YORK	LEEDS	BRISTOL

15/3

Who is *Blue Peter*'s longest-serving female presenter of all time?

ANTHEA TURNER	DIANE-LOUISE JORDAN	KONNIE HUQ	ROCHELLE HUMES
VALERIE SINGLETON	VALERIE SINGLETON	VALERIE SINGLETON	MARY

15/4

George Valentin, Peppy Miller and a dog named Jack are characters in which Oscar-winning film?

THE WIZARD OF OZ	*BOYHOOD*	*THE ARTIST*	*TITANIC*
THE ARTIST	*DIGBY*	*ARTISTS*	*A FISH CALLED WANDA*

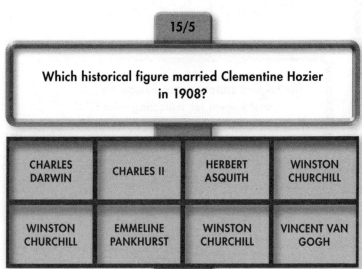

15/5

Which historical figure married Clementine Hozier in 1908?

CHARLES DARWIN	CHARLES II	HERBERT ASQUITH	WINSTON CHURCHILL
WINSTON CHURCHILL	EMMELINE PANKHURST	WINSTON CHURCHILL	VINCENT VAN GOGH

15/6

Which word that represents a letter of the NATO phonetic alphabet is also the name of a national capital city?

QUEBEC	LIMA	LIMA	QUEBEC
JAVA	LIMA	BERLIN	SYDNEY

THINK TANKERS' WORST ANSWERS

The Filipina stateswoman Imelda Marcos is best known for collecting what?

Think Tanker:
Stamps

Correct Answer:
Shoes

Richard Starkey is the real name of which pop star?

Think Tanker:
Ritchie from Five

Correct Answer:
Ringo Starr

QUESTIONS

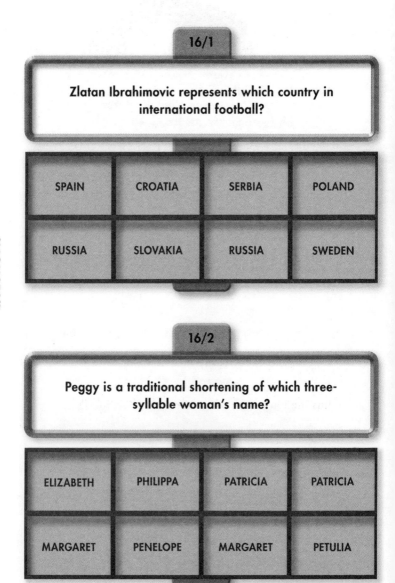

16/1

Zlatan Ibrahimovic represents which country in international football?

SPAIN	CROATIA	SERBIA	POLAND
RUSSIA	SLOVAKIA	RUSSIA	SWEDEN

16/2

Peggy is a traditional shortening of which three-syllable woman's name?

ELIZABETH	PHILIPPA	PATRICIA	PATRICIA
MARGARET	PENELOPE	MARGARET	PETULIA

16/3

What does the 'J' stand for in the name of the author J K Rowling?

JOANNE	JESSICA	JANE	JANIS
JOANNA	JEAN	JENNY	JUDITH

QUESTIONS

16/4

As of 1 January 2016, which European country has the longest-serving monarch after the UK?

SWEDEN	BELGIUM	MONACO	NORWAY
SPAIN	BELGIUM	SPAIN	DENMARK

QUESTIONS

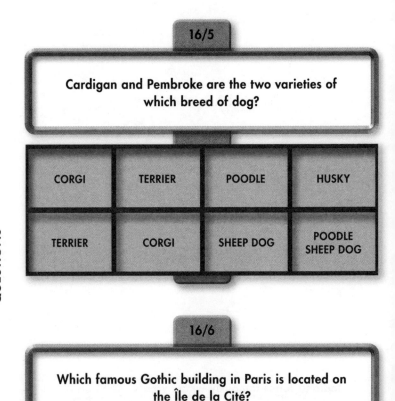

16/5

Cardigan and Pembroke are the two varieties of which breed of dog?

CORGI	TERRIER
POODLE	HUSKY
TERRIER	CORGI
SHEEP DOG	POODLE SHEEP DOG

16/6

Which famous Gothic building in Paris is located on the Île de la Cité?

NOTRE DAME	THE LOUVRE
ARC DE TRIOMPHE	PACIFIC ENLIGHT
NOTRE DAME	NOTRE DAME
ST PETER'S CATHEDRAL	THE LOUVRE

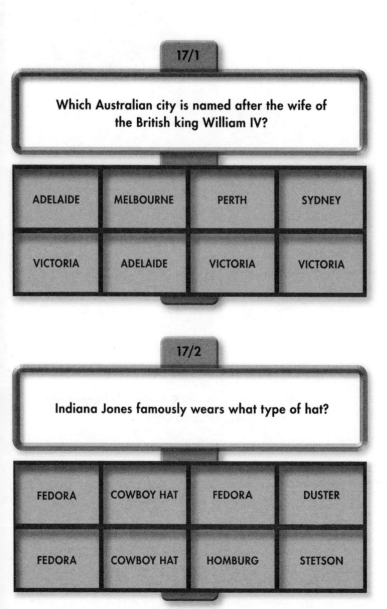

17/1

Which Australian city is named after the wife of the British king William IV?

| ADELAIDE | MELBOURNE | PERTH | SYDNEY |
| VICTORIA | ADELAIDE | VICTORIA | VICTORIA |

17/2

Indiana Jones famously wears what type of hat?

| FEDORA | COWBOY HAT | FEDORA | DUSTER |
| FEDORA | COWBOY HAT | HOMBURG | STETSON |

17/3

'Mad Dogs and Englishmen' is a song by which British songwriter?

| ELTON JOHN | JESSIE J | ED SHEERAN | NOËL COWARD |
| OSCAR WILDE | DAVID BOWIE | GERSHWIN | JOHNNY DAVRO |

QUESTIONS

17/4

Gotham is an old-fashioned name for which city?

| NEW YORK | LONDON | NEW YORK | NEW YORK |
| BERLIN | GOTHENBURG | GOTHENBURG | LINCOLN |

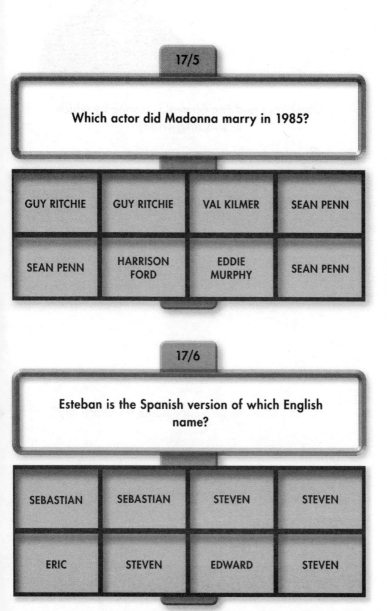

17/5

Which actor did Madonna marry in 1985?

GUY RITCHIE	GUY RITCHIE	VAL KILMER	SEAN PENN
SEAN PENN	HARRISON FORD	EDDIE MURPHY	SEAN PENN

17/6

Esteban is the Spanish version of which English name?

SEBASTIAN	SEBASTIAN	STEVEN	STEVEN
ERIC	STEVEN	EDWARD	STEVEN

QUESTIONS

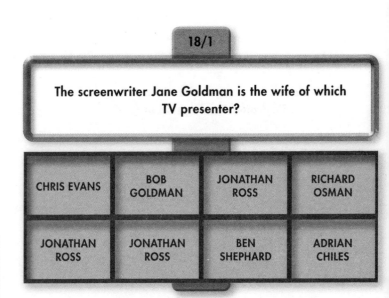

18/1

The screenwriter Jane Goldman is the wife of which TV presenter?

CHRIS EVANS	BOB GOLDMAN	JONATHAN ROSS	RICHARD OSMAN
JONATHAN ROSS	JONATHAN ROSS	BEN SHEPHARD	ADRIAN CHILES

18/2

Which Asian animal's name translates into English as 'large cat bear'?

PANDA	LION	TIGER	BAGHEERA
TIGER	PANDA	PANDA	TIGER

18/3

Who played the arms dealer Richard Roper in the TV drama *The Night Manager*?

MARK RYLANCE	TOM HICKMAN	JAMES FAULKNER	BEN KINGSLEY
HUGH LAURIE	HUGH LAURIE	JAMES O'FLYNN	TOM HIDDLESTON

18/4

Which city hosted its very first Formula One race in June 2016?

DUBAI	DUBAI	BAHRAIN	MONACO
MADRID	BAKU	BEIJING	MOSCOW

QUESTIONS

71

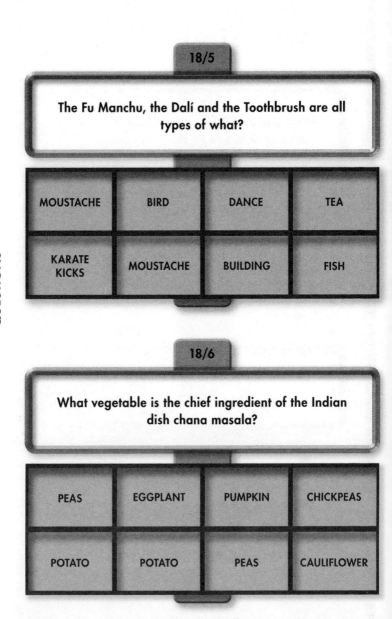

18/5

The Fu Manchu, the Dalí and the Toothbrush are all types of what?

MOUSTACHE	BIRD	DANCE	TEA
KARATE KICKS	MOUSTACHE	BUILDING	FISH

18/6

What vegetable is the chief ingredient of the Indian dish chana masala?

PEAS	EGGPLANT	PUMPKIN	CHICKPEAS
POTATO	POTATO	PEAS	CAULIFLOWER

THINK TANKERS' WORST ANSWERS

What is a 'Blue Peter', after which the long-running children's TV show was named?

Think Tanker:
Badge

Correct Answer:
Flag

What is the surname of the British singer Adele?

Think Tanker:
Bangermaker

Correct Answer:
Adkins

19/1

In 1963, who became the first British person to be declared an honorary citizen of the United States?

| THE QUEEN | WINSTON CHURCHILL | QUENTIN CRISP | MARGARET THATCHER |
| THE QUEEN | WINSTON CHURCHILL | MARGARET THATCHER | THE QUEEN |

19/2

The waterway called the Golden Horn forms part of which modern-day city?

| RIO DE JANEIRO | PALM SPRINGS | SINGAPORE | AMSTERDAM |
| SOUTHAMPTON | SAN FRANCISCO | VENICE | ISTANBUL |

QUESTIONS

19/3

How many players are there in a standard netball team?

SIX	SEVEN	SIX	SEVEN
EIGHT	SEVEN	SIX	EIGHT

19/4

Which pop band, who had a hit with 'I'm Free' in 1990, were named after a character from *The Clangers*?

SOUP DRAGONS	WHAM!	THE FARM	DOCTOR NO
THE SINGING RINGING TREE	GEORGE AND THE WHISTLE	BRONSKI BEAT	SOUP DRAGONS

19/5

Which sign of the zodiac is sometimes called 'The Archer'?

SAGITTARIUS	VIRGO	SAGITTARIUS	ARIES
ARIES	ARIES	CAPRICORN	SAGITTARIUS

19/6

The 2015 women's US Open Final was the first tennis Grand Slam Final to be contested between two players from which country?

RUSSIA	ITALY	USA	RUSSIA
UK	FRANCE	USA	FRANCE

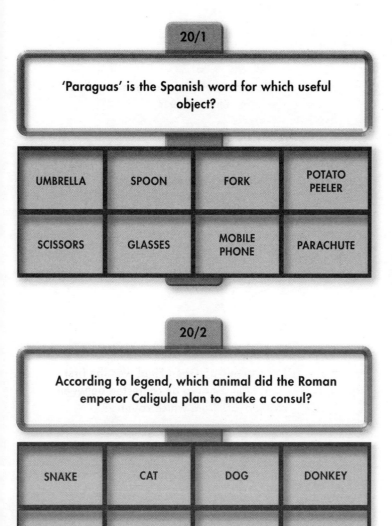

20/1

'Paraguas' is the Spanish word for which useful object?

| UMBRELLA | SPOON | FORK | POTATO PEELER |
| SCISSORS | GLASSES | MOBILE PHONE | PARACHUTE |

20/2

According to legend, which animal did the Roman emperor Caligula plan to make a consul?

| SNAKE | CAT | DOG | DONKEY |
| LION | CAT | HORSE | EAGLE |

QUESTIONS

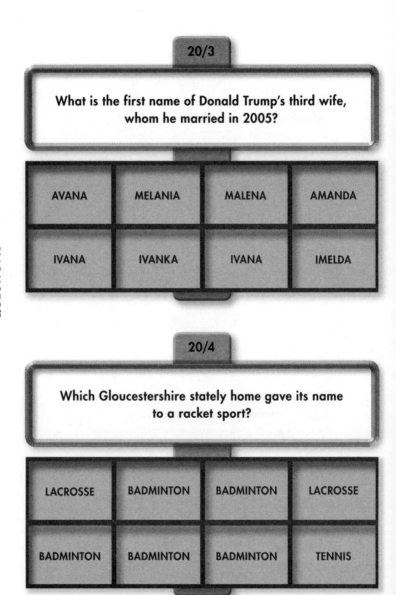

20/3

What is the first name of Donald Trump's third wife, whom he married in 2005?

| AVANA | MELANIA | MALENA | AMANDA |
| IVANA | IVANKA | IVANA | IMELDA |

20/4

Which Gloucestershire stately home gave its name to a racket sport?

| LACROSSE | BADMINTON | BADMINTON | LACROSSE |
| BADMINTON | BADMINTON | BADMINTON | TENNIS |

20/5

Which Premier League team played its final home match at the Boleyn Ground in May 2016?

WEST HAM UNITED	BOURNEMOUTH	WEST HAM UNITED	LEICESTER CITY
TOTTENHAM HOTSPUR	EVERTON	WEST HAM UNITED	BOURNEMOUTH

QUESTIONS

20/6

The type of pasta called 'orecchiette' literally translates as 'little...' what?

HEARTS	SHELLS	EARS	SHELLS
EGGS	CIRCLES	EARS	BALLS

QUESTIONS

21/1

According to the results of an Ipsos MORI poll released in 2016, what is the UK's most trusted profession?

TEACHER	DOCTOR	THE CLERGY	POSTMAN
DOCTOR	DOCTOR	DOCTOR	NURSE

21/2

Since leaving the band, who is the only one of the Spice Girls to have never had a UK no.1 single?

MEL B	VICTORIA BECKHAM	GERI HALLIWELL	GERI HALLIWELL
VICTORIA BECKHAM	VICTORIA BECKHAM	VICTORIA BECKHAM	MEL B

21/3

Which man appears on the new plastic £5 Bank of England bank note, issued in 2016?

WINSTON CHURCHILL	CHARLES DARWIN	WINSTON CHURCHILL	CHARLES DARWIN
CHARLES DARWIN	CHARLES DARWIN	THOMAS TELFORD	ISAMBARD KINGDOM BRUNEL

QUESTIONS

21/4

Who is the only person to have sung a *James Bond* theme song and also to have appeared during the opening credits?

MADONNA	TINA TURNER	SHIRLEY BASSEY	SHIRLEY BASSEY
ADELE	ALICIA KEYS	ADELE	SHEENA EASTON

QUESTIONS

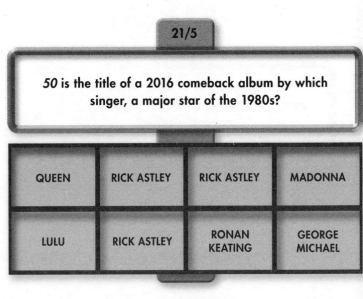

21/5

50 is the title of a 2016 comeback album by which singer, a major star of the 1980s?

QUEEN	RICK ASTLEY	RICK ASTLEY	MADONNA
LULU	RICK ASTLEY	RONAN KEATING	GEORGE MICHAEL

21/6

The Barossa Valley is one of the oldest wine regions of which country?

FRANCE	ENGLAND	AUSTRALIA	ITALY
ITALY	ITALY	SPAIN	CHILE

THINK TANKERS' WORST ANSWERS

In 2015, who was selected as the Tory party's official candidate for London's next mayoral election?

Think Tanker:
Susan Boyle

Correct Answer:
Zac Goldsmith

Whose autobiography is entitled *Losing My Virginity*?

Think Tanker:
Jordan

Correct Answer:
Richard Branson

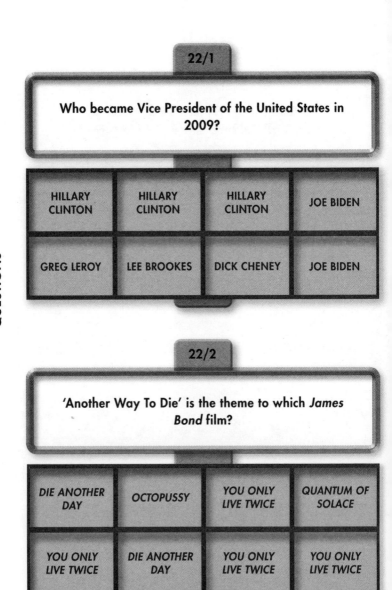

22/1

Who became Vice President of the United States in 2009?

HILLARY CLINTON	HILLARY CLINTON	HILLARY CLINTON	JOE BIDEN
GREG LEROY	LEE BROOKES	DICK CHENEY	JOE BIDEN

22/2

'Another Way To Die' is the theme to which *James Bond* film?

DIE ANOTHER DAY	OCTOPUSSY	YOU ONLY LIVE TWICE	QUANTUM OF SOLACE
YOU ONLY LIVE TWICE	DIE ANOTHER DAY	YOU ONLY LIVE TWICE	YOU ONLY LIVE TWICE

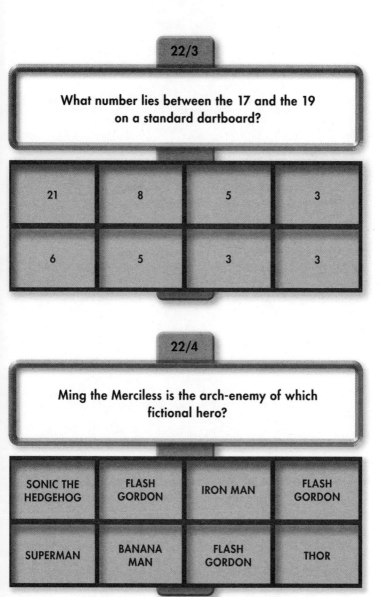

22/3

What number lies between the 17 and the 19 on a standard dartboard?

21	8	5	3
6	5	3	3

22/4

Ming the Merciless is the arch-enemy of which fictional hero?

SONIC THE HEDGEHOG	FLASH GORDON	IRON MAN	FLASH GORDON
SUPERMAN	BANANA MAN	FLASH GORDON	THOR

QUESTIONS

22/5

The paw-paw is a fruit better known by what name?

GRAPEFRUIT	PINEAPPLE
MANGO	PAPAYA

GRAPEFRUIT	PINEAPPLE
STARFRUIT	JACKFRUIT

22/6

In which country are the *Mad Max* series of films set?

AUSTRALIA	AUSTRALIA
MEXICO	USA

USA	AUSTRALIA
AUSTRALIA	USA

23/1

Which member of the royal family joined the
Marines in 1986?

| PRINCE EDWARD | PRINCE ANDREW | PRINCE ANDREW | PRINCE CHARLES |
| PRINCE EDWARD | PRINCE ANDREW | PRINCE ANDREW | PRINCE ANDREW |

23/2

Which British singer had six UK Top 10 albums in
2016?

| ADELE | SAM SMITH | ADELE | DAVID BOWIE |
| SAM SMITH | MEGHAN TRAINOR | SAM SMITH | DAVID BOWIE |

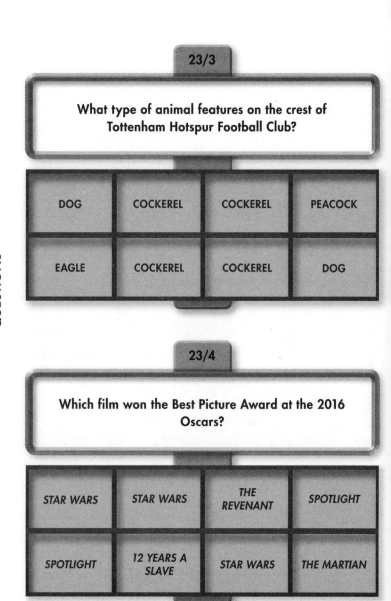

23/3

What type of animal features on the crest of Tottenham Hotspur Football Club?

| DOG | COCKEREL | COCKEREL | PEACOCK |
| EAGLE | COCKEREL | COCKEREL | DOG |

23/4

Which film won the Best Picture Award at the 2016 Oscars?

| STAR WARS | STAR WARS | THE REVENANT | SPOTLIGHT |
| SPOTLIGHT | 12 YEARS A SLAVE | STAR WARS | THE MARTIAN |

23/5

Including the wisdom teeth, how many teeth do most adult humans have?

32	32	28	32
36	36	32	24

23/6

The Bangles song 'Manic Monday' was written by which other singer?

CYNDI LAUPER	ELTON JOHN	CRAIG DAVID	PRINCE
PRINCE	LULU	PAUL MCCARTNEY	ALISON MOYET

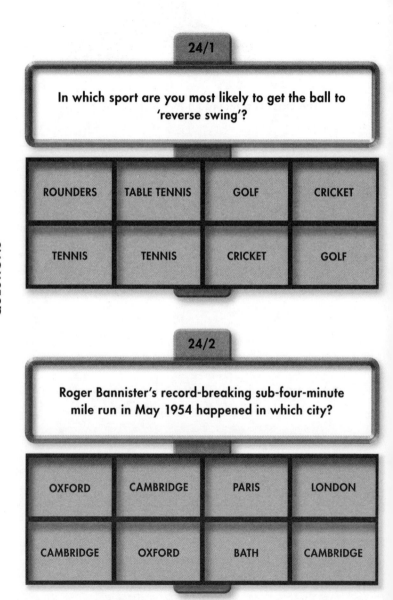

24/1

In which sport are you most likely to get the ball to 'reverse swing'?

ROUNDERS	TABLE TENNIS	GOLF	CRICKET
TENNIS	TENNIS	CRICKET	GOLF

24/2

Roger Bannister's record-breaking sub-four-minute mile run in May 1954 happened in which city?

OXFORD	CAMBRIDGE	PARIS	LONDON
CAMBRIDGE	OXFORD	BATH	CAMBRIDGE

QUESTIONS

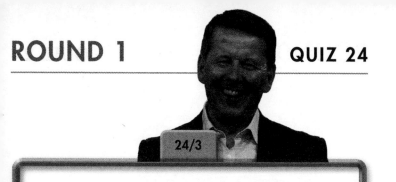

24/3

The Eiger is a mountain in which country?

SWITZERLAND	AUSTRIA	NEPAL	GREECE
AUSTRIA	CANADA	SWITZERLAND	AUSTRIA

24/4

Prince William and Prince Harry allegedly filmed cameo roles for which film franchise in 2016?

JAMES BOND	STAR WARS	THE LEGEND OF TARZAN	ABSOLUTELY FABULOUS
STAR WARS	STAR WARS	STAR WARS	STAR WARS

QUESTIONS

QUESTIONS

24/5

In the board game Cluedo what colour is Mrs Peacock?

BLUE	BLUE
RED	BLUE
GREEN	RED
PURPLE	PURPLE

24/6

Which snooker player is nicknamed the 'Jester from Leicester'?

STEVE DAVIS	STEPHEN HENDRY
JOHN VIRGO	RONNIE O'SULLIVAN
RONNIE O'SULLIVAN	JOHN VIRGO
PHIL TAYLOR	MARK SELBY

THINK TANKERS' WORST ANSWERS

Which breed of dog is named after a Mexican state?

Think Tanker:
Weimaraner

Correct Answer:
Chihuahua

'All animals are equal, but some animals are more equal than others' is a famous line from which book?

Think Tanker: Darwin's *The Origin of Species*

Correct Answer:
Orwell's *Animal Farm*

QUESTIONS

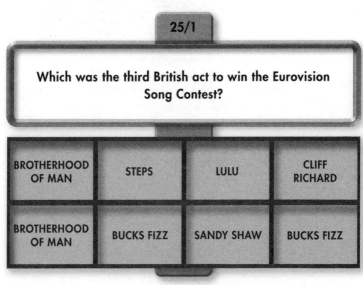

25/1

Which was the third British act to win the Eurovision Song Contest?

BROTHERHOOD OF MAN	STEPS	LULU	CLIFF RICHARD
BROTHERHOOD OF MAN	BUCKS FIZZ	SANDY SHAW	BUCKS FIZZ

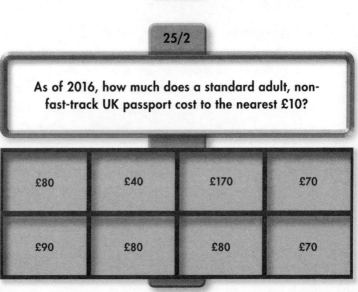

25/2

As of 2016, how much does a standard adult, non-fast-track UK passport cost to the nearest £10?

£80	£40	£170	£70
£90	£80	£80	£70

25/3

The ancient philosopher Socrates was a native of which city?

ROME	ATHENS	ROME	SYRACUSE
ATHENS	ATHENS	POMPEII	ATHENS

25/4

Which US state has the most electoral votes in a Presidential election?

TEXAS	CALIFORNIA	TEXAS	NEW HAMPSHIRE
CALIFORNIA	NEW YORK	CALIFORNIA	TEXAS

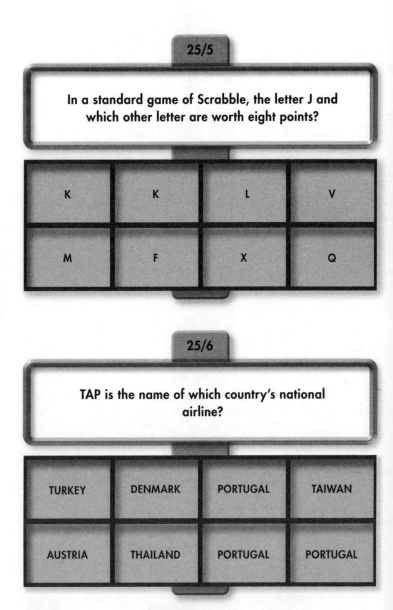

25/5

In a standard game of Scrabble, the letter J and which other letter are worth eight points?

K	K	L	V
M	F	X	Q

25/6

TAP is the name of which country's national airline?

TURKEY	DENMARK	PORTUGAL	TAIWAN
AUSTRIA	THAILAND	PORTUGAL	PORTUGAL

ROUND 1

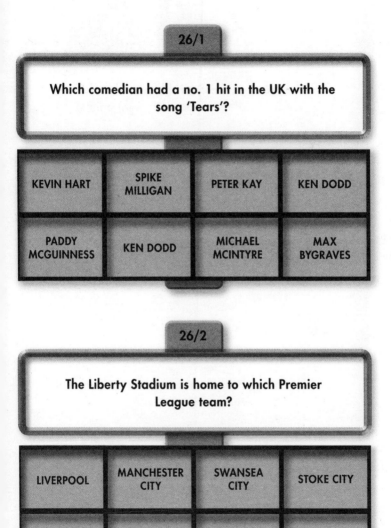

26/1

Which comedian had a no. 1 hit in the UK with the song 'Tears'?

KEVIN HART	SPIKE MILLIGAN	PETER KAY	KEN DODD
PADDY MCGUINNESS	KEN DODD	MICHAEL MCINTYRE	MAX BYGRAVES

26/2

The Liberty Stadium is home to which Premier League team?

LIVERPOOL	MANCHESTER CITY	SWANSEA CITY	STOKE CITY
ARSENAL	SWANSEA CITY	LEEDS	ARSENAL

QUESTIONS

QUESTIONS

26/3

Which species of seabird is sometimes called the 'sea parrot'?

SEAGULL	PUFFIN	PUFFIN	GANNET
SEAGULL	PUFFIN	PUFFIN	SEAGULL

26/4

In the book by Herman Melville, which species of whale is Moby Dick?

SPERM WHALE	HUMPBACK WHALE	SPERM WHALE	HUMPBACK WHALE
KILLER WHALE	BLUE WHALE	HUMPBACK WHALE	KILLER WHALE

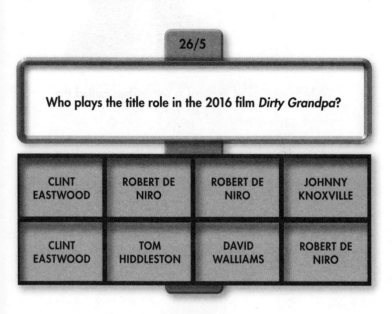

26/5

Who plays the title role in the 2016 film *Dirty Grandpa*?

CLINT EASTWOOD	ROBERT DE NIRO	ROBERT DE NIRO	JOHNNY KNOXVILLE
CLINT EASTWOOD	TOM HIDDLESTON	DAVID WALLIAMS	ROBERT DE NIRO

26/6

Worcestershire Beacon is the highest point in which of the UK's 43 official Areas of Outstanding Natural Beauty?

PEAK DISTRICT	BRECON BEACONS	PEAK DISTRICT	LAKE DISTRICT
PEAK DISTRICT	PEAK DISTRICT	PEAK DISTRICT	MALVERN HILLS

QUESTIONS

99

QUESTIONS

27/1

According to the official website of the US Social Security Administration, which biblical name was the most popular name given to American baby boys born in 2015?

JOSHUA	MICHAEL	JOHN	ABEL
JOSHUA	JESUS	NOAH	ADAM

27/2

Graphite is a form of which chemical element?

LEAD	STEEL	CARBON	GRANITE
LEAD	LEAD	CARBON	CARBON

27/3

Which US city was the main setting for the popular TV drama series *The Wire*?

BOSTON	BALTIMORE	BALTIMORE	CHICAGO
CHICAGO	WASHINGTON	CHICAGO	SEATTLE

27/4

The Tynwald, often said to be the oldest parliament in the world, is based on which island?

ISLE OF MAN	NEW ZEALAND	ICELAND	ISLE OF MAN
JERSEY	ISLE OF MAN	ISLE OF MAN	HONG KONG

27/5

'The Parish Boy's Progress' is the subtitle of which novel by Charles Dickens?

OLIVER TWIST	OLIVER TWIST	OLIVER TWIST	GREAT EXPECTATIONS
GREAT EXPECTATIONS	GREAT EXPECTATIONS	OLIVER TWIST	OLIVER TWIST

27/6

Emmental cheese is named after a river valley in which country?

HOLLAND	FRANCE	SWITZERLAND	GERMANY
SWITZERLAND	SWITZERLAND	SWITZERLAND	FRANCE

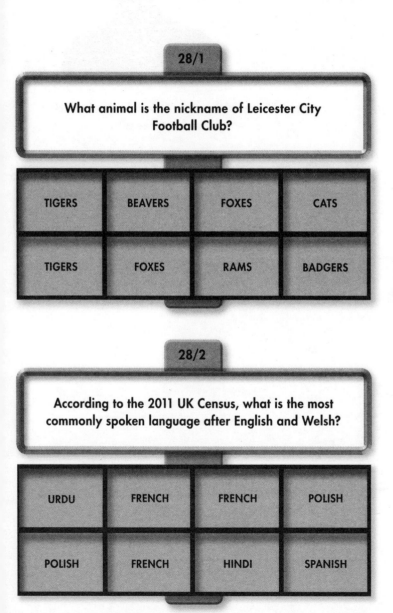

28/1

What animal is the nickname of Leicester City Football Club?

TIGERS	BEAVERS	FOXES	CATS
TIGERS	FOXES	RAMS	BADGERS

28/2

According to the 2011 UK Census, what is the most commonly spoken language after English and Welsh?

URDU	FRENCH	FRENCH	POLISH
POLISH	FRENCH	HINDI	SPANISH

QUESTIONS

QUESTIONS

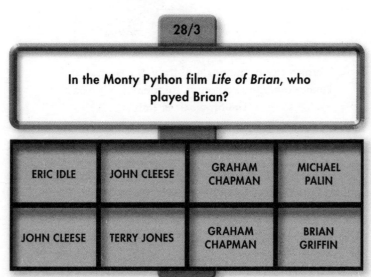

28/3

In the Monty Python film *Life of Brian*, who played Brian?

ERIC IDLE	JOHN CLEESE
GRAHAM CHAPMAN	MICHAEL PALIN
JOHN CLEESE	TERRY JONES
GRAHAM CHAPMAN	BRIAN GRIFFIN

28/4

Which middle name is shared by John Lennon and Gary Lineker?

ALBERT	FRANKLIN
STEPHEN	WINSTON
TOBY	EDWARD
MARK	LUKE

28/5

Which city in the north of Italy, the capital of the
Emilia-Romagna region, is sometimes referred to as
'The Stomach of Italy'?

SICILY	BOLOGNA	ROME	UMBRIA
ROME	ROME	MILAN	ROME

QUESTIONS

28/6

Whom did Muhammad Ali fight in the so-called
'Rumble in the Jungle'?

CASSIUS CLAY	HENRY COOPER	GEORGE FOREMAN	HENRY COOPER
ASHLEY JORDAN	MUHAMMAD ALI	GEORGE FOREMAN	GEORGE FOREMAN

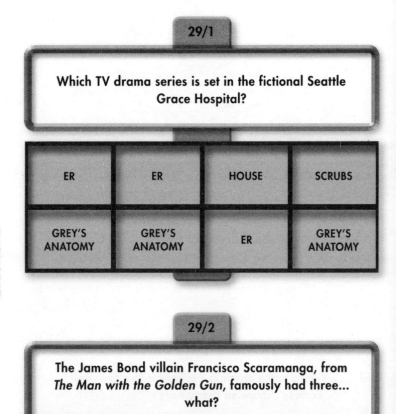

29/1

Which TV drama series is set in the fictional Seattle Grace Hospital?

ER	ER	HOUSE	SCRUBS
GREY'S ANATOMY	GREY'S ANATOMY	ER	GREY'S ANATOMY

29/2

The James Bond villain Francisco Scaramanga, from *The Man with the Golden Gun*, famously had three... what?

FINGERS	NIPPLES	EYES	NIPPLES
NIPPLES	NIPPLES	NIPPLES	FINGERS

29/3

Alesha Dixon was a member of which successful girl band?

MIS-TEEQ	SUGABABES	DESTINY'S CHILD	PUSSYCAT DOLLS
MIS-TEEQ	MIS-TEEQ	PUSSYCAT DOLLS	MIS-TEEQ

QUESTIONS

29/4

Which make of car is known for the 'Spirit of Ecstasy' figure on the bonnet of its models?

FERRARI	FIAT PUNTO	ROLLS-ROYCE	ROLLS-ROYCE
JAGUAR	ROLLS-ROYCE	SKODA	ROLLS-ROYCE

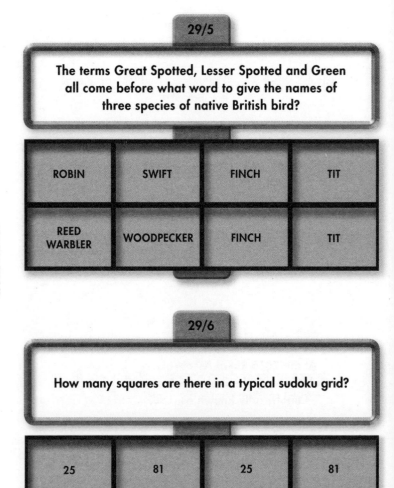

29/5

The terms Great Spotted, Lesser Spotted and Green all come before what word to give the names of three species of native British bird?

| ROBIN | SWIFT | FINCH | TIT |
| REED WARBLER | WOODPECKER | FINCH | TIT |

29/6

How many squares are there in a typical sudoku grid?

| 25 | 81 | 25 | 81 |
| 81 | 9 | 960 | 9 |

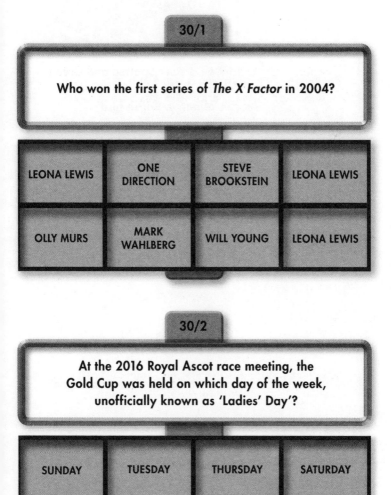

30/1

Who won the first series of *The X Factor* in 2004?

| LEONA LEWIS | ONE DIRECTION | STEVE BROOKSTEIN | LEONA LEWIS |
| OLLY MURS | MARK WAHLBERG | WILL YOUNG | LEONA LEWIS |

QUESTIONS

30/2

At the 2016 Royal Ascot race meeting, the Gold Cup was held on which day of the week, unofficially known as 'Ladies' Day'?

| SUNDAY | TUESDAY | THURSDAY | SATURDAY |
| THURSDAY | SATURDAY | THURSDAY | FRIDAY |

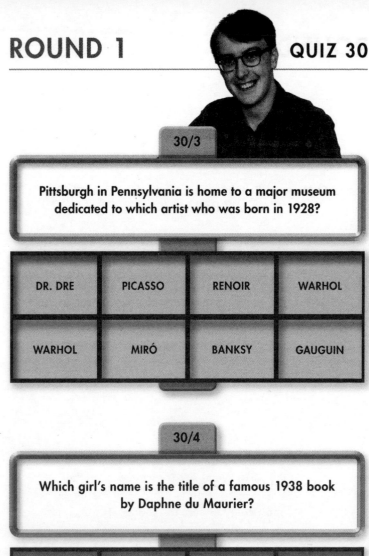

30/3

Pittsburgh in Pennsylvania is home to a major museum dedicated to which artist who was born in 1928?

DR. DRE	PICASSO	RENOIR	WARHOL
WARHOL	MIRÓ	BANKSY	GAUGUIN

QUESTIONS

30/4

Which girl's name is the title of a famous 1938 book by Daphne du Maurier?

REBECCA	EMMA	LOLA	ANNA
EMMA	BELLE	JACKIE	REBECCA

30/5

St Magnus, Britain's most northerly cathedral, lies on which group of islands?

HEBRIDES	SHETLAND ISLANDS	ISLE OF WIGHT	ORKNEY ISLANDS
CHANNEL ISLANDS	ORKNEY ISLANDS	HEBRIDES	SHETLAND ISLANDS

30/6

The word 'drizzy' is most associated with which rapper?

DIZZEE RASCAL	DRAKE	DRAKE	DIZZEE RASCAL
DRAKE	DIZZEE RASCAL	DIZZEE RASCAL	DR. DRE

THINK TANKERS' WORST ANSWERS

What name is given to newly born alligators?

Think Tanker: Dave

Correct Answer:
Hatchlings

Which boxer was the first man to win the BBC Sports Personality of the Year Award twice?

Think Tanker: Tim Henman

Correct Answer:
Henry Cooper

THINK TANKERS' WORST ANSWERS

What is Sherlock Holmes' London address?

Think Tanker: Scotland Yard

Correct Answer:
221B Baker St

Which member of the famous Cambridge spy ring held the position of Surveyor of the Queen's Pictures?

Think Tanker:
Hugh Bonneville

Correct Answer:
Anthony Blunt

ROUND 2

1/1

Which word, derived from the Italian for 'bartender', is given to someone who makes coffee for a living?

1/2

Which type of creature is Sven in the Disney film *Frozen*?

1/3

Which former *Coronation Street* actress played the role of the policewoman Catherine Cawood in the TV drama series *Happy Valley*?

1/4

In which film does Ben Stiller star as the gym owner White Goodman?

1/5

What does the 'H' stand for in the dating abbreviation GSOH?

1/6

Which hit single by Barry Manilow shares its name with a Brazilian beach and a New York nightclub?

1/7

In March 1836, the Alamo in Texas fell to the army of which country?

1/8

Who has scored more league goals for Arsenal Football Club than any other male player?

1/9

Which singer and former model memorably performed while hula-hooping at the Queen's Diamond Jubilee concert in 2012?

QUESTIONS

2/1

Dry ice is the solid form of which chemical compound?

2/2

Paul Rudd played which Marvel comics superhero in a 2015 film?

2/3

Ashley Banjo has found fame as the leader of which dance troupe?

2/4

Pinkie and Spicer are characters in which book by Graham Greene?

2/5

What colour is the traditional eye make-up kohl – particularly popular in eastern countries?

2/6

The tapas dish bacalao is traditionally made with which type of fish?

2/7

Gareth Bale left which club to join Real Madrid in 2013?

2/8

What was the title of Adele's first ever UK Top 40 hit single?

2/9

Which country, with coasts on the Black Sea and the Mediterranean Sea, has land in both Europe and Asia?

QUESTIONS

3/1

In which country was the radio DJ Zane Lowe born?

3/2

What is the name of the large flat-topped mountain that overlooks Cape Town?

3/3

Which two colours feature on the national flag of Poland?

3/4

The TV comedy series *Family Guy* is set in which fictional town?

3/5

Which Spanish city is the capital of the region of Catalonia?

3/6

What is the name of the world's first adhesive postage stamp, first used in May 1840?

3/7

Komodo Dragons are native to which country?

3/8

Which county cricket team play home matches in Birmingham?

3/9

In Thai cuisine, what type of food is tom yum?

QUESTIONS

4/1

Which Canadian ice hockey player was nicknamed 'The Great One'?

4/2

Absurd Person Singular and *A Chorus of Disapproval* are plays by which writer?

4/3

Who played the role of Lord Flashheart in the TV comedy series *Blackadder II*?

4/4

What is the meaning of the Latin word 'ego'?

4/5

Jamie Vardy was the top scorer for which Premier League football team in the 2015-16 season?

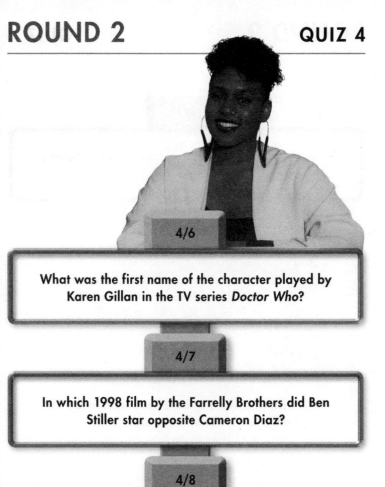

4/6

What was the first name of the character played by Karen Gillan in the TV series *Doctor Who*?

4/7

In which 1998 film by the Farrelly Brothers did Ben Stiller star opposite Cameron Diaz?

4/8

Which dance, that became popular in the 1920s, is named after a city in South Carolina?

4/9

In 2013, Greg Dyke became the chairman of which organization?

5/1

What is the capital city of Barbados?

5/2

'On the Street Where You Live' and 'The Rain in Spain' are songs from which musical?

5/3

With which band did Mary J Blige collaborate on the 2006 UK Top 10 hit single 'One'?

5/4

In 1913, the suffragette Emily Davison famously disrupted which major sporting event?

5/5

Tofu is traditionally made from what type of beans?

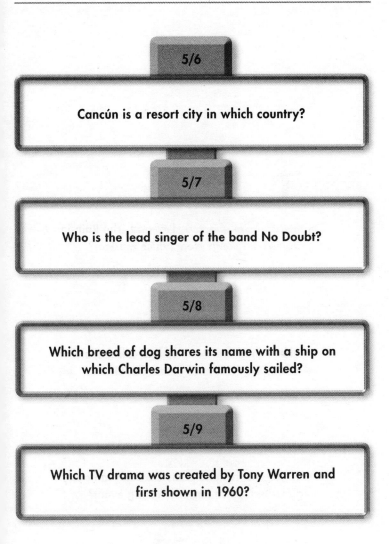

5/6

Cancún is a resort city in which country?

5/7

Who is the lead singer of the band No Doubt?

5/8

Which breed of dog shares its name with a ship on which Charles Darwin famously sailed?

5/9

Which TV drama was created by Tony Warren and first shown in 1960?

QUESTIONS

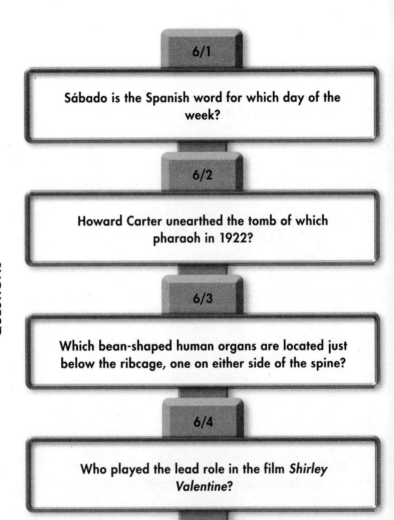

6/1

Sábado is the Spanish word for which day of the week?

6/2

Howard Carter unearthed the tomb of which pharaoh in 1922?

6/3

Which bean-shaped human organs are located just below the ribcage, one on either side of the spine?

6/4

Who played the lead role in the film *Shirley Valentine*?

6/5

The film *Pan's Labyrinth* is set in which European country?

6/6

What is Charlie's surname in the Roald Dahl book
Charlie and the Chocolate Factory?

6/7

Which metal, traditionally used to make darts, is
sometimes known as 'wolfram'?

6/8

Which soul singer plays the role of Mrs Murphy in
the 1980 film *The Blues Brothers*?

6/9

'Cogito ergo sum', meaning 'I think therefore I am',
is a famous quote by which philosopher?

QUESTIONS

QUESTIONS

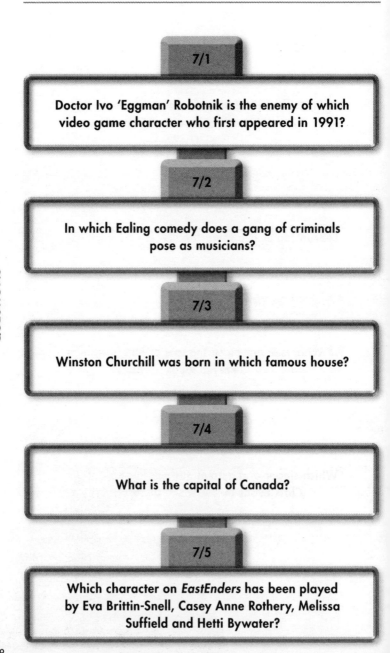

7/1

Doctor Ivo 'Eggman' Robotnik is the enemy of which video game character who first appeared in 1991?

7/2

In which Ealing comedy does a gang of criminals pose as musicians?

7/3

Winston Churchill was born in which famous house?

7/4

What is the capital of Canada?

7/5

Which character on *EastEnders* has been played by Eva Brittin-Snell, Casey Anne Rothery, Melissa Suffield and Hetti Bywater?

7/6

Knight, Death and the Devil and *Saint Jerome In His Study* are notable works by which German artist?

7/7

LeBron James is a famous name in which sport?

7/8

What is Jeremy's surname in the TV sitcom *Peep Show*?

7/9

Which singer and actress married Chris Evans in 2001?

LEN

QUESTIONS

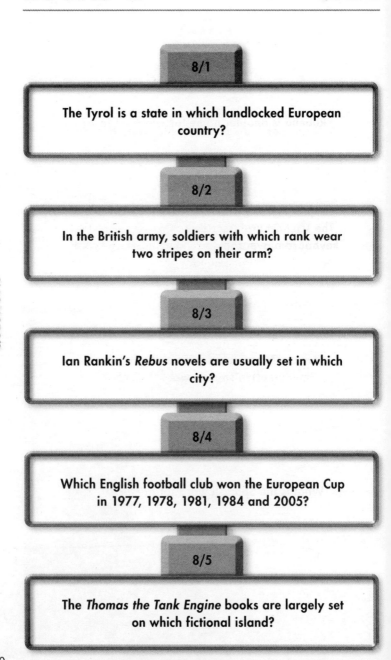

8/1

The Tyrol is a state in which landlocked European country?

8/2

In the British army, soldiers with which rank wear two stripes on their arm?

8/3

Ian Rankin's *Rebus* novels are usually set in which city?

8/4

Which English football club won the European Cup in 1977, 1978, 1981, 1984 and 2005?

8/5

The *Thomas the Tank Engine* books are largely set on which fictional island?

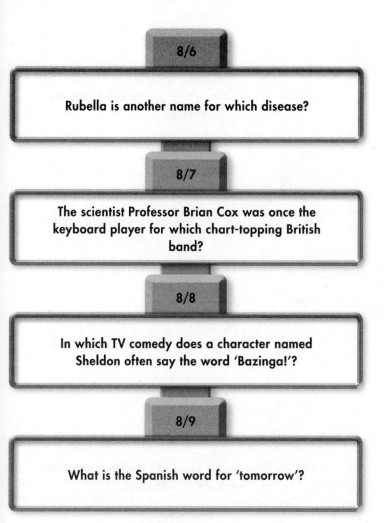

8/6

Rubella is another name for which disease?

8/7

The scientist Professor Brian Cox was once the keyboard player for which chart-topping British band?

8/8

In which TV comedy does a character named Sheldon often say the word 'Bazinga!'?

8/9

What is the Spanish word for 'tomorrow'?

QUESTIONS

9/1

Who played Al Pacino's father in the 1972 film *The Godfather*?

9/2

Which word, meaning to deceive someone, is also a type of boiled sweet, typically striped and flavoured with peppermint?

9/3

Which singer, born in 1911, was known as 'The Queen of Gospel'?

9/4

What is the popular name of the Royal Military Academy in Berkshire?

9/5

Which news presenter, born in Trinidad, was awarded a knighthood in 1999 for his services to journalism?

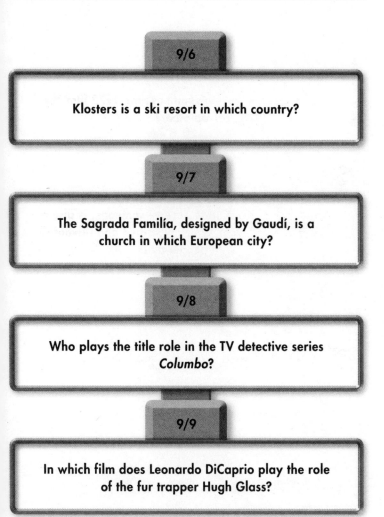

9/6

Klosters is a ski resort in which country?

9/7

The Sagrada Família, designed by Gaudí, is a church in which European city?

9/8

Who plays the title role in the TV detective series *Columbo*?

9/9

In which film does Leonardo DiCaprio play the role of the fur trapper Hugh Glass?

QUESTIONS

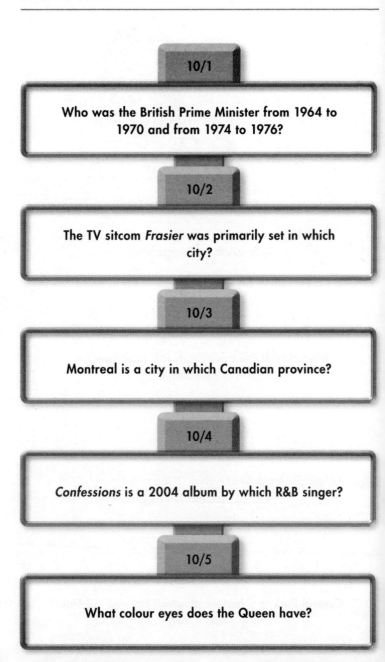

QUESTIONS

10/1

Who was the British Prime Minister from 1964 to 1970 and from 1974 to 1976?

10/2

The TV sitcom *Frasier* was primarily set in which city?

10/3

Montreal is a city in which Canadian province?

10/4

Confessions is a 2004 album by which R&B singer?

10/5

What colour eyes does the Queen have?

10/6

'Bind off', 'purl' and 'selvage' are commonly used terms in which craft?

10/7

Who played the title role in the 1958 Hammer horror film *Dracula*?

10/8

In *EastEnders*, who killed Lucy Beale?

10/9

Central Park is a feature of which borough of New York City?

QUESTIONS

11/1

What do the initials ECG stand for in terms of human medicine?

11/2

Bob Marley was born on which island?

11/3

The Valley of the Kings is a famous tourist area in which African country?

11/4

Which part of the Spanish coastline has a name that means 'wild coast' when translated into English?

11/5

'Hob' and 'Jill' are the names for the male and female of which small mammal?

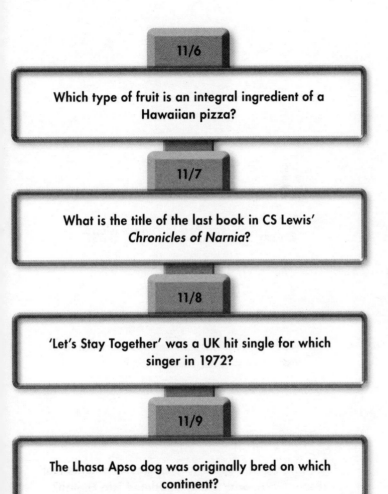

11/6

Which type of fruit is an integral ingredient of a Hawaiian pizza?

11/7

What is the title of the last book in CS Lewis' *Chronicles of Narnia*?

11/8

'Let's Stay Together' was a UK hit single for which singer in 1972?

11/9

The Lhasa Apso dog was originally bred on which continent?

QUESTIONS

12/1

Ibiza and Mallorca are part of which group of Spanish islands?

12/2

Martin Luther King famously gave his 'I have a dream' speech in which city in 1963?

12/3

Which ferry port is the closest French town to England?

12/4

The name of the drink sherry is derived from that of which city in Spain?

12/5

Which Welsh politician, born in November 1897, is regarded as the chief architect of the National Health Service?

12/6

In which country was the entrepreneur Elon Musk born?

12/7

Which former captain of the West Indies cricket team was nicknamed Super Cat?

12/8

Who is the narrator of the TV show *Come Dine With Me*?

12/9

Which businessman owns the exclusive resort of Necker Island in the Caribbean?

13/1

Which male British athlete won gold medals in the 110-metres hurdles at both the 1993 and 1999 World Athletics Championships?

13/2

Which type of Mexican dish takes its name from the Spanish for 'little donkey'?

13/3

Who played the title role in the 1976 western *The Outlaw Josey Wales*?

13/4

Which American city is often referred to as the 'Birthplace of Jazz'?

13/5

Which type of pizza is said to be named after a queen of Italy?

13/6

What was the title of Justin Bieber's first ever UK Top 10 hit single?

13/7

Who was the first person to be voted off *Strictly Come Dancing* in 2015?

13/8

The birthplace of the writer Joseph Conrad is in which modern-day country?

13/9

Sandra Bullock won an Oscar for her role in which film?

QUESTIONS

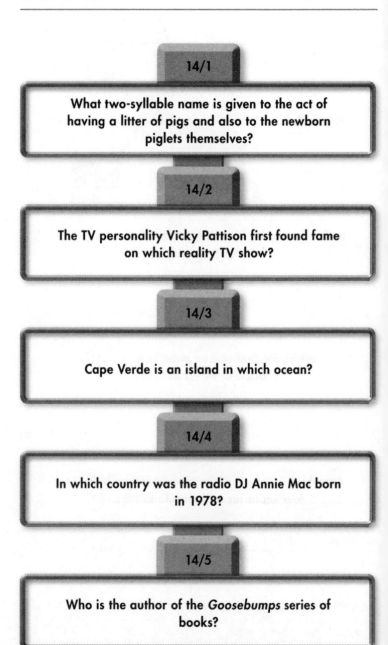

QUESTIONS

14/1

What two-syllable name is given to the act of having a litter of pigs and also to the newborn piglets themselves?

14/2

The TV personality Vicky Pattison first found fame on which reality TV show?

14/3

Cape Verde is an island in which ocean?

14/4

In which country was the radio DJ Annie Mac born in 1978?

14/5

Who is the author of the *Goosebumps* series of books?

14/6

Riga is the capital and largest city of which country?

14/7

In the *Thomas the Tank Engine* books, what colour is the engine called James?

14/8

Which TV chef is the daughter of a former Chancellor of the Exchequer?

14/9

Bara brith is a type of fruit bread from which of the four countries of the United Kingdom?

QUESTIONS

15/1

In Greek mythology, Icarus fell to his death after flying too close to what?

15/2

In humans, which glandular organ behind the stomach produces insulin?

15/3

The 'Hallelujah Chorus' is a famous choral work by which composer?

15/4

In the Super Mario computer games, what is the name of Mario's brother?

15/5

In which TV comedy did Rowan Atkinson play a policeman named Raymond Fowler?

15/6

Cyclops, Storm and Beast have all been long-term members of which superhero team?

15/7

What was the first South American city to win the right to host the Summer Olympic Games?

15/8

Jamie Foxx won an Oscar for his role in which film?

15/9

18 June 2015 marked the 200th anniversary of which famous battle?

QUESTIONS

16/1

What is the more common name of the patella bone in the human body?

16/2

The Australian Eddie Jones was named coach of England in which sport in 2015?

16/3

In ballet, what is a 'grand jeté'?

16/4

Justin Trudeau was elected Prime Minister of which country in 2015?

16/5

The quadriceps muscles are in which part of the human body?

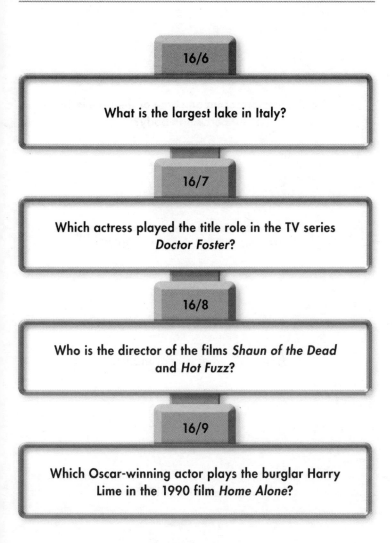

16/6

What is the largest lake in Italy?

16/7

Which actress played the title role in the TV series *Doctor Foster*?

16/8

Who is the director of the films *Shaun of the Dead* and *Hot Fuzz*?

16/9

Which Oscar-winning actor plays the burglar Harry Lime in the 1990 film *Home Alone*?

QUESTIONS

QUESTIONS

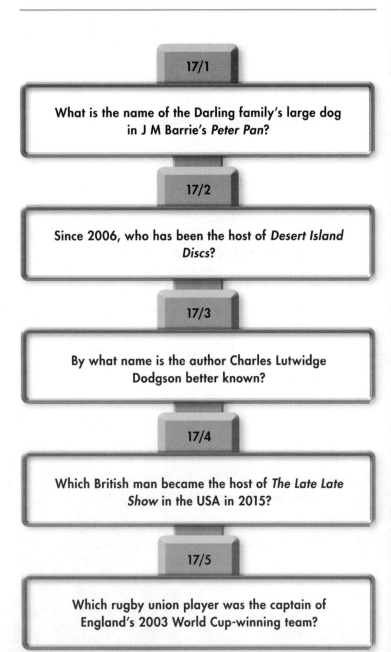

17/1

What is the name of the Darling family's large dog in J M Barrie's *Peter Pan*?

17/2

Since 2006, who has been the host of *Desert Island Discs*?

17/3

By what name is the author Charles Lutwidge Dodgson better known?

17/4

Which British man became the host of *The Late Late Show* in the USA in 2015?

17/5

Which rugby union player was the captain of England's 2003 World Cup-winning team?

17/6

The Øresund Bridge links which two countries?

17/7

The word 'thermidor' is most commonly used in connection with which type of shellfish?

17/8

Prince Philip was born on which island?

17/9

Which is the closest planet to the sun in our solar system?

18/1

The Normandy speciality of calvados is a type of brandy traditionally made with which fruit?

18/2

The four main members of The Goons comedy team were Peter Sellers, Michael Bentine, Spike Milligan and which other man?

18/3

Which famous building, opened in 1973, was designed by the architect Jørn Utzon to resemble the sails of a ship?

18/4

Which song, a signature tune of Etta James, did Beyoncé sing at the inauguration of Barack Obama?

18/5

The businessman Claude Littner joined the cast of which TV reality show in 2015?

18/6

In which TV drama series do Terrence Howard and Taraji P Henson play characters named Lucious and 'Cookie' Lyon?

18/7

The Manzanares river flows through which European capital city?

18/8

Who co-created and provides many of the voices for the TV comedy series *Family Guy*?

18/9

In the film *Scarface*, the character Tony Montana famously says 'Say hello to my little...' what?

19/1

Who directed the horror films *A Nightmare on Elm Street* and *Scream*?

19/2

'Tit Willow' and 'Three Little Maids' are songs from which work by Gilbert & Sullivan?

19/3

What was the first *James Bond* theme tune to be sung by Shirley Bassey?

19/4

The oath that was traditionally taken by newly qualified doctors takes its name from that of which Ancient Greek physician?

19/5

What was the title of David Bowie's first ever UK Top 40 hit single?

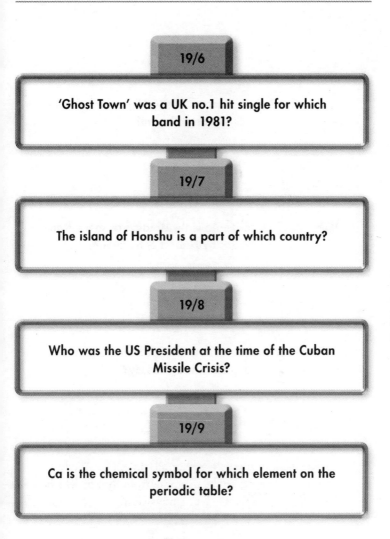

19/6

'Ghost Town' was a UK no.1 hit single for which band in 1981?

19/7

The island of Honshu is a part of which country?

19/8

Who was the US President at the time of the Cuban Missile Crisis?

19/9

Ca is the chemical symbol for which element on the periodic table?

QUESTIONS

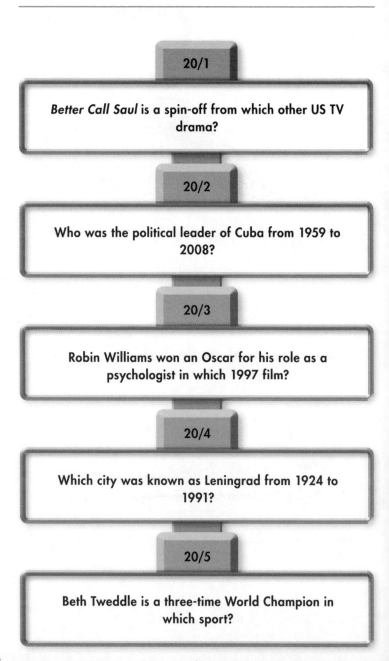

20/1

Better Call Saul is a spin-off from which other US TV drama?

20/2

Who was the political leader of Cuba from 1959 to 2008?

20/3

Robin Williams won an Oscar for his role as a psychologist in which 1997 film?

20/4

Which city was known as Leningrad from 1924 to 1991?

20/5

Beth Tweddle is a three-time World Champion in which sport?

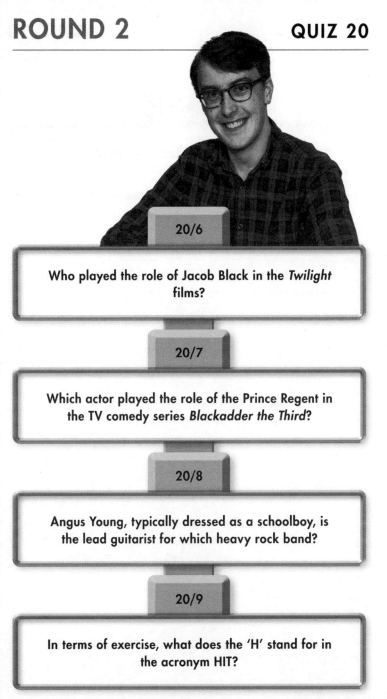

20/6

Who played the role of Jacob Black in the *Twilight* films?

20/7

Which actor played the role of the Prince Regent in the TV comedy series *Blackadder the Third*?

20/8

Angus Young, typically dressed as a schoolboy, is the lead guitarist for which heavy rock band?

20/9

In terms of exercise, what does the 'H' stand for in the acronym HIT?

QUESTIONS

155

ROUND 2

QUIZ 21

QUESTIONS

21/1

The film *No Country for Old Men* was based on a book by which author?

21/2

Greg Rutherford won a World Athletics Championship gold medal in which event in 2015?

21/3

In the *Harry Potter* books, by what name is Tom Riddle better known?

21/4

The Last Judgement by Michelangelo is a famous fresco in which building?

21/5

Which female tennis player won the Wimbledon, Australian Open and French Open titles in 2015?

21/6

What was the surname of the Secretary of State for War who was at the centre of a political scandal in 1963?

21/7

The island of Mauritius is in which ocean?

21/8

The opening scenes of the Bond film *Spectre* are set in a 'Day of the Dead' celebration in which country?

21/9

Which Latin phrase, meaning 'bounteous mother', is said to refer to someone's old school?

QUESTIONS

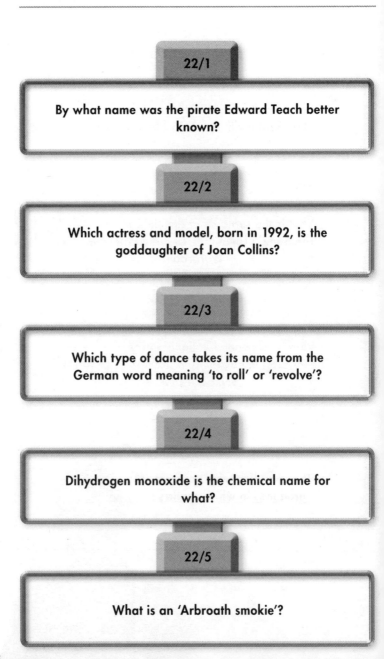

22/1

By what name was the pirate Edward Teach better known?

22/2

Which actress and model, born in 1992, is the goddaughter of Joan Collins?

22/3

Which type of dance takes its name from the German word meaning 'to roll' or 'revolve'?

22/4

Dihydrogen monoxide is the chemical name for what?

22/5

What is an 'Arbroath smokie'?

22/6

Who played the role of the stranded astronaut Mark Watney in the 2015 film *The Martian*?

22/7

What is the surname of the children who visit Narnia in CS Lewis' *The Lion the Witch and the Wardrobe*?

22/8

What is suspended in liquid in Damien Hirst's *The Physical Impossibility of Death in the Mind of Someone Living*?

22/9

The sparkling wine prosecco is produced in which country?

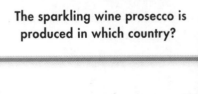

23/1

By what one word name are an orchestra's kettledrums also known?

23/2

The singer Dido featured on the single 'Stan' by which other recording artist?

23/3

The word 'doppelgänger', meaning an exact duplicate of a person, is a word from which language?

23/4

What does the 'U' stand for in the name of the Middle Eastern country UAE?

23/5

Which British pop star was born in what is now Kosovo in 1990?

23/6

The original 1976 film *Rocky* was set in which city?

23/7

In the DC comics, what is the first name of Batman's butler?

23/8

Going Home, Season of Passion and *Matters of the Heart* are books by which American author?

23/9

Who co-wrote the TV comedy series *Gavin and Stacey* with Ruth Jones?

QUESTIONS

24/1

What does the letter 'D' stand for in the building material MDF?

24/2

Which type of bird is the official emblem of the United States of America?

24/3

Which is the only national flag in the world that is neither square nor rectangular?

24/4

Kane and Abel and *The Prodigal Daughter* are books by which author?

24/5

Which controversial dating website had its membership database hacked and partially published on the web in August 2015?

24/6

Mo Farah won Olympic gold medals in the 5,000 metres and which other event at the 2012 Olympics?

24/7

'What's Happening Brother' and 'Mercy Mercy Me (The Ecology)' are songs from which 1971 Marvin Gaye album?

24/8

The tango dance originated on which continent?

24/9

In which Will Ferrell film does Ed Asner play Father Christmas?

THINK
TANK

ROUND 2

QUESTIONS

25/1

Who wrote and directed the 2015 film *The Hateful Eight*?

25/2

Which board game was invented by Alfred Mosher Butts and originally called Lexiko?

25/3

Which British actor played both Ronnie and Reggie Kray in the 2015 film *Legend*?

25/4

Which TV drama series is based on a book by Piper Kerman?

25/5

Which is the largest of the Balearic Islands?

25/6

'Roads? Where we're going, we don't need roads.'
is the final line in which film?

25/7

Which *Friends* actor played Robert Kardashian
in the 2016 US drama series *The People v. O.J.
Simpson: American Crime Story*?

25/8

Port of Spain is the capital city of which Caribbean
country?

25/9

Which hit song by Gerry Rafferty features a famous
saxophone solo that was falsely claimed to be
played by the presenter Bob Holness?

QUESTIONS

QUESTIONS

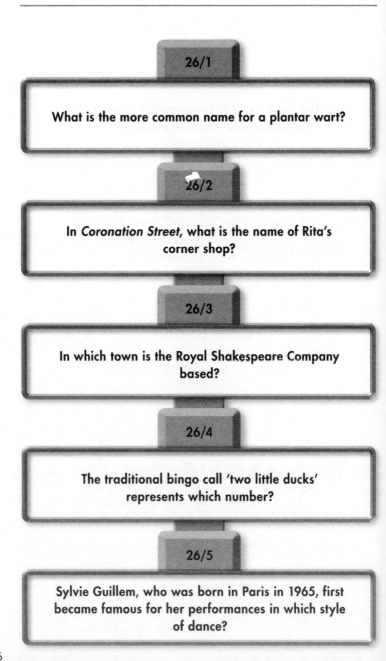

26/1

What is the more common name for a plantar wart?

26/2

In *Coronation Street*, what is the name of Rita's corner shop?

26/3

In which town is the Royal Shakespeare Company based?

26/4

The traditional bingo call 'two little ducks' represents which number?

26/5

Sylvie Guillem, who was born in Paris in 1965, first became famous for her performances in which style of dance?

26/6

The Knicks, or Knickerbockers, are an NBA basketball team based in which US city?

26/7

Bruce Delamitri is the central character of which Ben Elton novel that shares its name with a snack food?

26/8

Alice Springs is a town in which territory of Australia?

26/9

How many hoops are there on a standard croquet lawn?

ROUND 2

27/1

By what three-letter nickname was the 1950s US President Dwight D Eisenhower known?

27/2

At the 2012 Olympics, the showjumping and other equestrian events were held in which London park?

27/3

In which Shakespeare play does Polonius famously say 'neither a borrower nor a lender be' and 'to thine own self be true'?

27/4

The line-dancing song '5,6,7,8' was the first single for which 1990s group?

27/5

Which city, on the banks of the river Ness, is considered the capital of the Highlands?

27/6

What colour rose is traditionally the symbol of the House of Lancaster?

27/7

Which entertainer took over from Tommy Trinder as the host of *Sunday Night at the London Palladium* in 1958?

27/8

In genetics, each human cell normally contains how many pairs of chromosomes?

27/9

The glockenspiel is a musical instrument that belongs to what section of an orchestra?

QUESTIONS

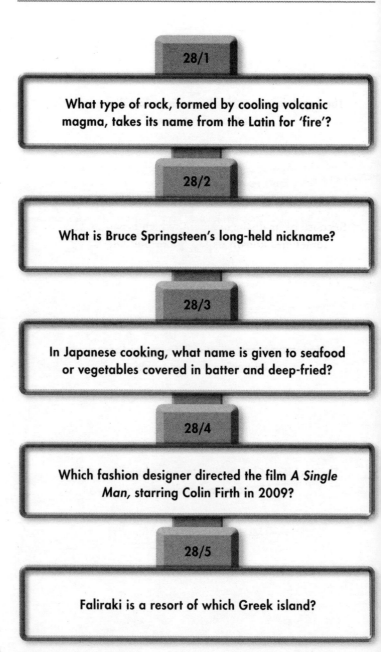

28/1

What type of rock, formed by cooling volcanic magma, takes its name from the Latin for 'fire'?

28/2

What is Bruce Springsteen's long-held nickname?

28/3

In Japanese cooking, what name is given to seafood or vegetables covered in batter and deep-fried?

28/4

Which fashion designer directed the film *A Single Man*, starring Colin Firth in 2009?

28/5

Faliraki is a resort of which Greek island?

28/6

The legal suspense thriller *A Time To Kill* was which author's first novel?

28/7

Because of its distinctive coat, which breed of dog is sometimes known as the 'plum-pudding dog'?

28/8

How many metres are there in one lap of an Olympic athletics track?

28/9

The architect Christopher Wren is buried in which London building?

QUESTIONS

29/1

The word 'nephritic' refers specifically to which organ of the human body?

29/2

Which member of the royal family is a patron of the Royal Pigeon Racing Association and the National Flying Club?

29/3

The world's largest cruise ship, which set off on its first sea trial in March 2016, is called *Harmony of the...* what?

29/4

Who does David Mitchell play in the 2016 sitcom *Upstart Crow*?

29/5

In T S Eliot's poem *The Waste Land*, what is said to be the cruellest month?

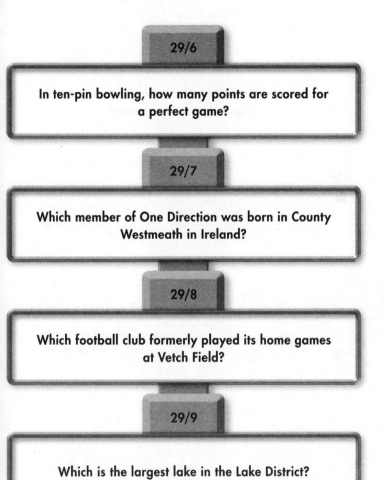

29/6

In ten-pin bowling, how many points are scored for a perfect game?

29/7

Which member of One Direction was born in County Westmeath in Ireland?

29/8

Which football club formerly played its home games at Vetch Field?

29/9

Which is the largest lake in the Lake District?

QUESTIONS

30/1

Ted Danson played Sam Malone in which US sitcom, set in a Boston bar?

30/2

Who was the leader of the Huns when they invaded Italy in 452?

30/3

What was the title of Jamie Oliver's first cookery series on British television?

30/4

Which dish, consisting of a pizza base folded over and filled, takes its name from the Italian for 'trouser leg'?

30/5

Which fashion designer launched his revolutionary 'New Look' in 1947?

30/6

Which noble gas takes its name from the Greek word for 'new'?

30/7

The Dada art movement takes its name from the French word for which traditional children's toy?

30/8

How many canine teeth does an adult usually have?

30/9

What is the largest living species of penguin?

THINK TANKERS' WORST ANSWERS

For what does the 'K' stand in the name of the author J K Rowling?

Think Tanker: Kas

Correct Answer:
Kathleen

What name was given to the 'stick' used by the comedian Ken Dodd in his act?

Think Tanker: Rod

Correct Answer:
Tickling Stick

THINK TANKERS' WORST ANSWERS

Complete the title of Public Enemy's 1988 UK Top 20 single, 'Don't Believe…'.

Think Tanker: In Love

Correct Answer:
The Hype

What is the English equivalent of the Spanish dessert called arroz con leche?

Think Tanker: Spotted dick

Correct Answer:
Rice pudding

ROUND 3

QUESTIONS

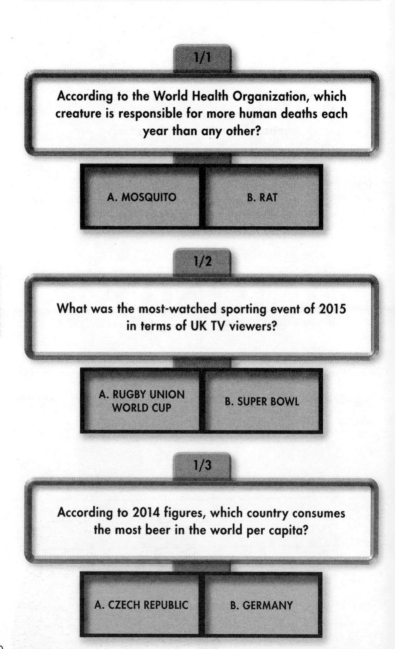

1/1

According to the World Health Organization, which creature is responsible for more human deaths each year than any other?

| A. MOSQUITO | B. RAT |

1/2

What was the most-watched sporting event of 2015 in terms of UK TV viewers?

| A. RUGBY UNION WORLD CUP | B. SUPER BOWL |

1/3

According to 2014 figures, which country consumes the most beer in the world per capita?

| A. CZECH REPUBLIC | B. GERMANY |

1/4

According to the Internet Movie Database, as of December 2015, which *EastEnders* character has appeared in the most episodes?

A. DOT COTTON

B. PHIL MITCHELL

1/5

Which poet is often credited with writing the lyrics of the song 'Auld Lang Syne'?

A. WILLIAM SHAKESPEARE

B. ROBERT BURNS

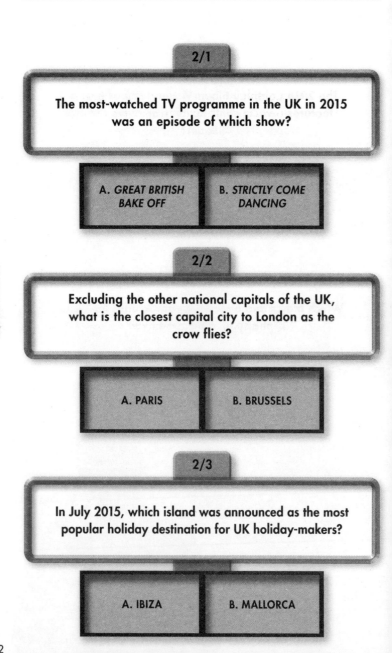

2/1

The most-watched TV programme in the UK in 2015 was an episode of which show?

A. *GREAT BRITISH BAKE OFF*

B. *STRICTLY COME DANCING*

2/2

Excluding the other national capitals of the UK, what is the closest capital city to London as the crow flies?

A. PARIS

B. BRUSSELS

2/3

In July 2015, which island was announced as the most popular holiday destination for UK holiday-makers?

A. IBIZA

B. MALLORCA

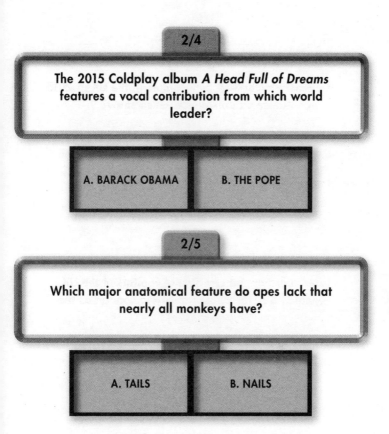

2/4

The 2015 Coldplay album *A Head Full of Dreams* features a vocal contribution from which world leader?

A. BARACK OBAMA

B. THE POPE

2/5

Which major anatomical feature do apes lack that nearly all monkeys have?

A. TAILS

B. NAILS

QUESTIONS

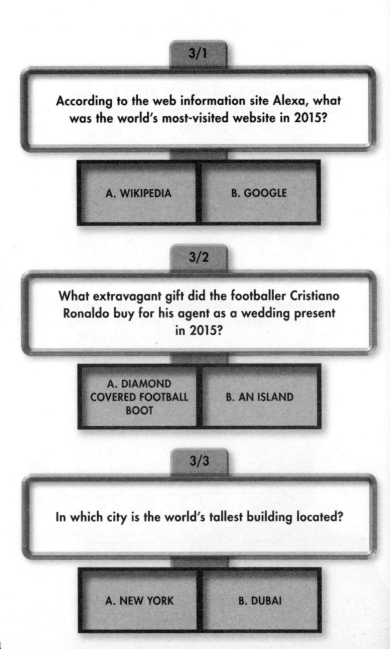

3/1

According to the web information site Alexa, what was the world's most-visited website in 2015?

A. WIKIPEDIA

B. GOOGLE

3/2

What extravagant gift did the footballer Cristiano Ronaldo buy for his agent as a wedding present in 2015?

A. DIAMOND COVERED FOOTBALL BOOT

B. AN ISLAND

3/3

In which city is the world's tallest building located?

A. NEW YORK

B. DUBAI

3/4

According to the Society of Motor Manufacturers and Traders, what was the most popular colour for new cars bought in the UK in 2014?

A. WHITE

B. RED

3/5

What event takes place almost every year on a British farm owned by the Eavis family?

A. CHEESE ROLLING

B. GLASTONBURY FESTIVAL

QUESTIONS

LEN

185

QUESTIONS

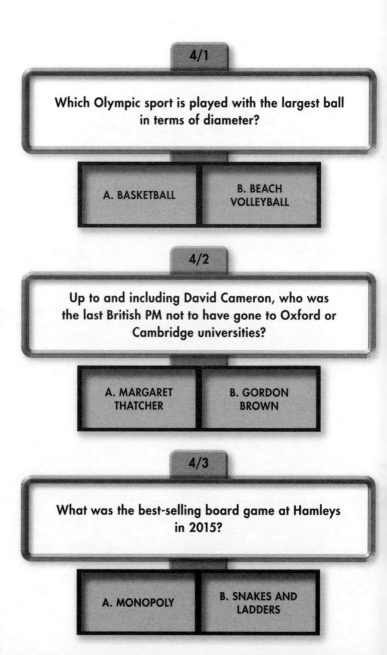

4/1

Which Olympic sport is played with the largest ball in terms of diameter?

A. BASKETBALL

B. BEACH VOLLEYBALL

4/2

Up to and including David Cameron, who was the last British PM not to have gone to Oxford or Cambridge universities?

A. MARGARET THATCHER

B. GORDON BROWN

4/3

What was the best-selling board game at Hamleys in 2015?

A. MONOPOLY

B. SNAKES AND LADDERS

4/4

The steamed dumplings known as dim sum are a speciality of which country?

| A. CHINA | B. VIETNAM |

4/5

Who was the first male celebrity winner of *Strictly Come Dancing*?

| A. MARK RAMPRAKASH | B. DARREN GOUGH |

QUESTIONS

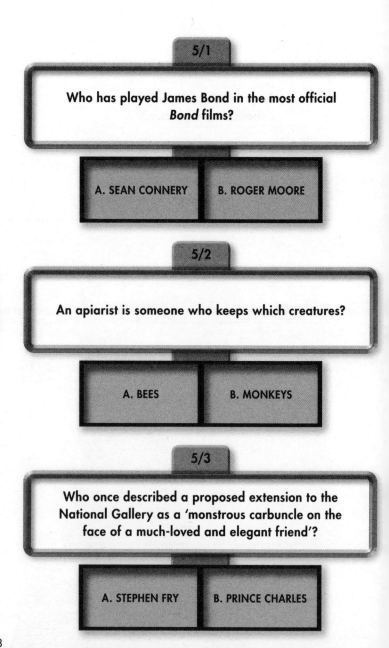

5/1

Who has played James Bond in the most official *Bond* films?

A. SEAN CONNERY

B. ROGER MOORE

5/2

An apiarist is someone who keeps which creatures?

A. BEES

B. MONKEYS

5/3

Who once described a proposed extension to the National Gallery as a 'monstrous carbuncle on the face of a much-loved and elegant friend'?

A. STEPHEN FRY

B. PRINCE CHARLES

5/4

What was the profession of Harry Hill before he became a comedian?

A. ACCOUNTANT

B. DOCTOR

5/5

The platypus is native to which continent?

A. AUSTRALIA

B. SOUTH AMERICA

QUESTIONS

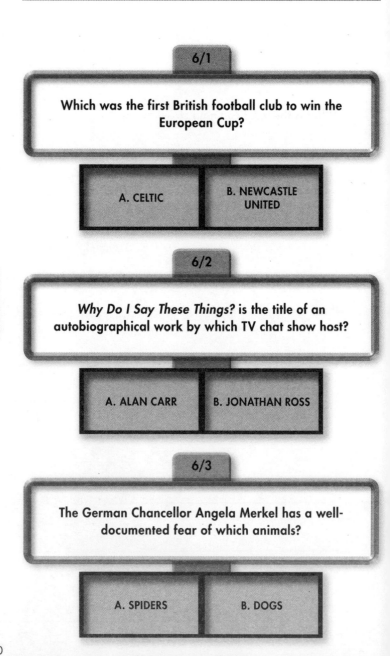

6/1

Which was the first British football club to win the European Cup?

A. CELTIC

B. NEWCASTLE UNITED

6/2

Why Do I Say These Things? is the title of an autobiographical work by which TV chat show host?

A. ALAN CARR

B. JONATHAN ROSS

6/3

The German Chancellor Angela Merkel has a well-documented fear of which animals?

A. SPIDERS

B. DOGS

6/4

What is the most common street name in the UK?

A. HIGH STREET   B. CHURCH STREET

6/5

Which country has won the Women's Football World Cup more than any other?

A. GERMANY   B. USA

QUESTIONS

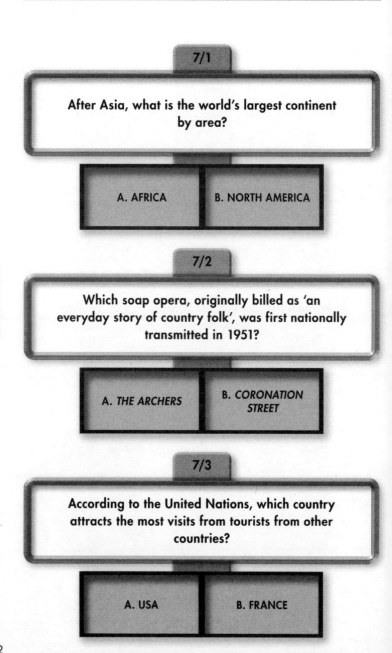

7/1

After Asia, what is the world's largest continent by area?

A. AFRICA

B. NORTH AMERICA

7/2

Which soap opera, originally billed as 'an everyday story of country folk', was first nationally transmitted in 1951?

A. *THE ARCHERS*

B. *CORONATION STREET*

7/3

According to the United Nations, which country attracts the most visits from tourists from other countries?

A. USA

B. FRANCE

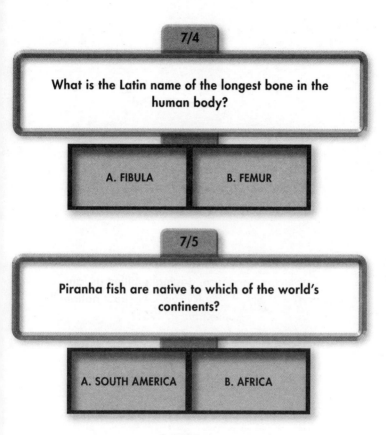

7/4

What is the Latin name of the longest bone in the human body?

A. FIBULA

B. FEMUR

7/5

Piranha fish are native to which of the world's continents?

A. SOUTH AMERICA

B. AFRICA

QUESTIONS

193

QUESTIONS

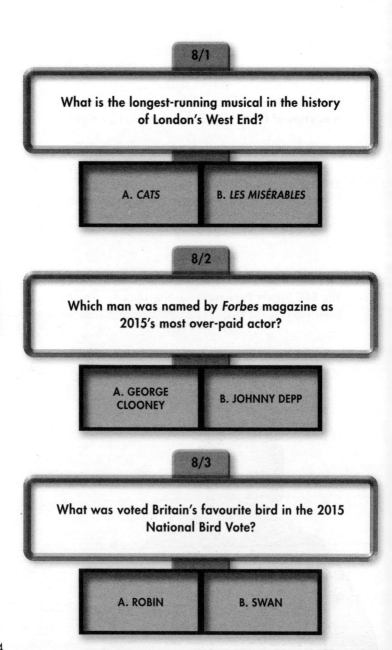

8/1

What is the longest-running musical in the history of London's West End?

A. *CATS*

B. *LES MISÉRABLES*

8/2

Which man was named by *Forbes* magazine as 2015's most over-paid actor?

A. GEORGE CLOONEY

B. JOHNNY DEPP

8/3

What was voted Britain's favourite bird in the 2015 National Bird Vote?

A. ROBIN

B. SWAN

8/4

Which politician did Boris Johnson once describe as 'a mixture of Harry Houdini and a greased piglet'?

| A. KEN LIVINGSTONE | B. TONY BLAIR |

8/5

The BBC Sports Personality of the Year Award has been won on the most occasions by participants in which sport?

| A. ATHLETICS | B. FOOTBALL |

QUESTIONS

PETER

9/1

In 2003, it was suggested in the media that the *Harry Potter* character Dobby bore a striking resemblance to which world leader?

A. ANGELA MERKEL

B. VLADIMIR PUTIN

9/2

According to *Forbes* magazine, who was the highest-paid sportsman from the British Isles in 2015?

A. RORY MCILROY

B. LEWIS HAMILTON

9/3

Which member of the Royal family reportedly set up a fake Facebook account under the name of Spike Wells?

A. PRINCE CHARLES

B. PRINCE HARRY

9/4

With a total audience of 7.2 million viewers, what was the most watched television programme on Christmas Day 2015?

A. *THE QUEEN'S CHRISTMAS MESSAGE*

B. *DOWNTON ABBEY*

9/5

According to *The Guardian* website, who was the UK's best-selling children's author of 2015?

A. DAVID WALLIAMS

B. JACQUELINE WILSON

QUESTIONS

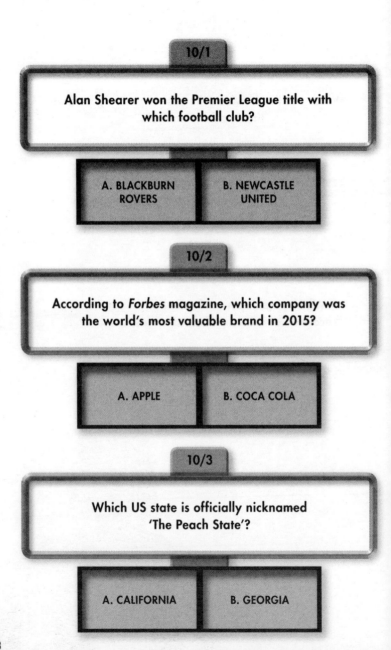

10/1

Alan Shearer won the Premier League title with which football club?

A. BLACKBURN ROVERS

B. NEWCASTLE UNITED

10/2

According to *Forbes* magazine, which company was the world's most valuable brand in 2015?

A. APPLE

B. COCA COLA

10/3

Which US state is officially nicknamed 'The Peach State'?

A. CALIFORNIA

B. GEORGIA

10/4

Which sea lies between the east coast of Egypt and the Arabian Peninsula?

A. DEAD SEA

B. RED SEA

10/5

Which pop singer performed at the wedding reception of Prince William and Kate Middleton?

A. ELTON JOHN

B. ELLIE GOULDING

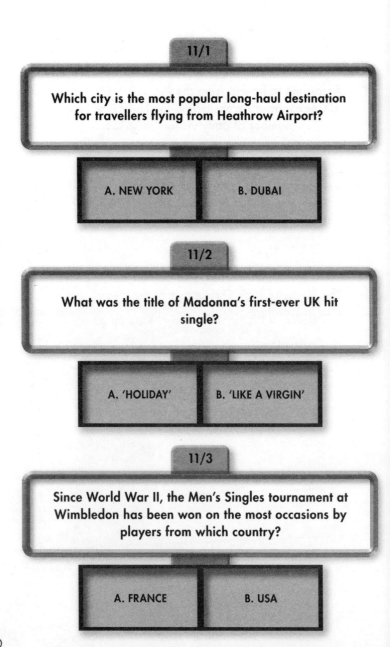

11/1

Which city is the most popular long-haul destination for travellers flying from Heathrow Airport?

A. NEW YORK

B. DUBAI

11/2

What was the title of Madonna's first-ever UK hit single?

A. 'HOLIDAY'

B. 'LIKE A VIRGIN'

11/3

Since World War II, the Men's Singles tournament at Wimbledon has been won on the most occasions by players from which country?

A. FRANCE

B. USA

11/4

According to figures from the *Press Gazette*, which UK newspaper's website had the highest average number of daily visitors in 2015?

| A. *THE SUN* | B. *DAILY MAIL* |

11/5

The 20-metre-high Christmas tree that stands each year in Trafalgar Square is typically an example of which species of tree?

| A. SPRUCE | B. CYPRESS |

QUESTIONS

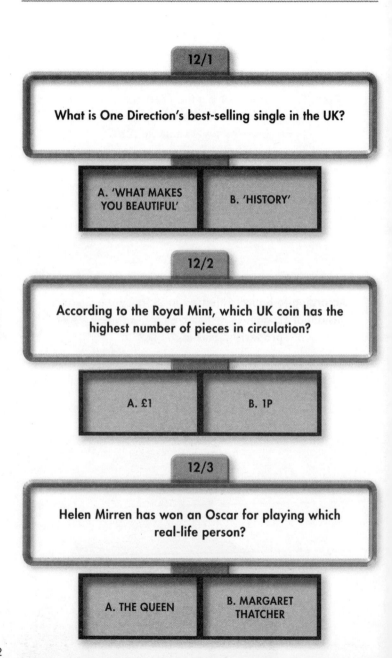

12/1

What is One Direction's best-selling single in the UK?

A. 'WHAT MAKES YOU BEAUTIFUL'

B. 'HISTORY'

12/2

According to the Royal Mint, which UK coin has the highest number of pieces in circulation?

A. £1

B. 1P

12/3

Helen Mirren has won an Oscar for playing which real-life person?

A. THE QUEEN

B. MARGARET THATCHER

12/4

Parkhurst Prison is located on which island?

A. ISLE OF MAN   B. ISLE OF WIGHT

12/5

According to figures released in 2015 by the London School of Economics, which country has the highest property prices in the world?

A. UK   B. MONACO

QUESTIONS

203

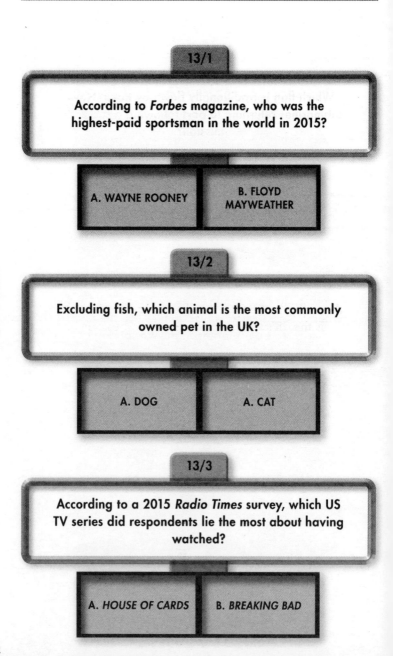

13/1

According to *Forbes* magazine, who was the highest-paid sportsman in the world in 2015?

A. WAYNE ROONEY

B. FLOYD MAYWEATHER

13/2

Excluding fish, which animal is the most commonly owned pet in the UK?

A. DOG

A. CAT

13/3

According to a 2015 *Radio Times* survey, which US TV series did respondents lie the most about having watched?

A. *HOUSE OF CARDS*

B. *BREAKING BAD*

13/4

Which flag is traditionally flown by Royal Navy submarines returning to port following a successful mission?

A. BLACK FLAG

B. JOLLY ROGER

13/5

According to the 2015 *Sunday Times* Rich List, who is the UK's richest young singer or musician?

A. ADELE

B. ED SHEERAN

QUESTIONS

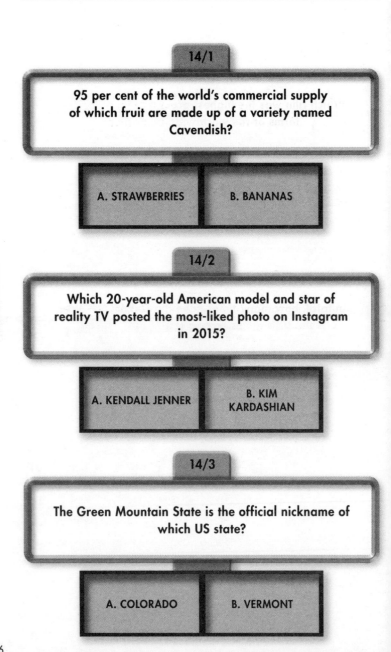

14/1

95 per cent of the world's commercial supply of which fruit are made up of a variety named Cavendish?

A. STRAWBERRIES

B. BANANAS

14/2

Which 20-year-old American model and star of reality TV posted the most-liked photo on Instagram in 2015?

A. KENDALL JENNER

B. KIM KARDASHIAN

14/3

The Green Mountain State is the official nickname of which US state?

A. COLORADO

B. VERMONT

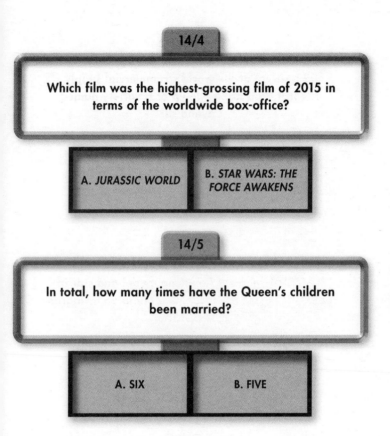

14/4

Which film was the highest-grossing film of 2015 in terms of the worldwide box-office?

A. JURASSIC WORLD

B. STAR WARS: THE FORCE AWAKENS

14/5

In total, how many times have the Queen's children been married?

A. SIX

B. FIVE

QUESTIONS

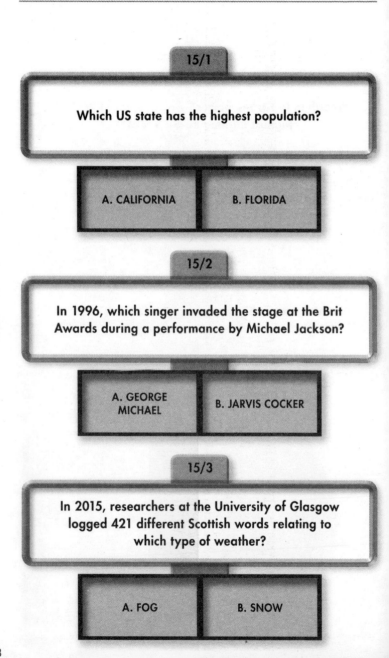

QUESTIONS

15/1

Which US state has the highest population?

A. CALIFORNIA

B. FLORIDA

15/2

In 1996, which singer invaded the stage at the Brit Awards during a performance by Michael Jackson?

A. GEORGE MICHAEL

B. JARVIS COCKER

15/3

In 2015, researchers at the University of Glasgow logged 421 different Scottish words relating to which type of weather?

A. FOG

B. SNOW

15/4

According to *Forbes* magazine, who was the world's highest-earning model in 2015?

| A. GISELE BÜNDCHEN | B. NAOMI CAMPBELL |

15/5

Which actress has been nominated for the most acting Oscars?

| A. MERYL STREEP | B. JUDI DENCH |

QUESTIONS

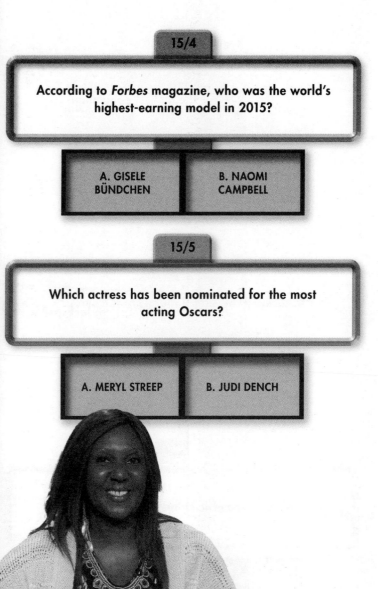

209

ROUND 3

QUESTIONS

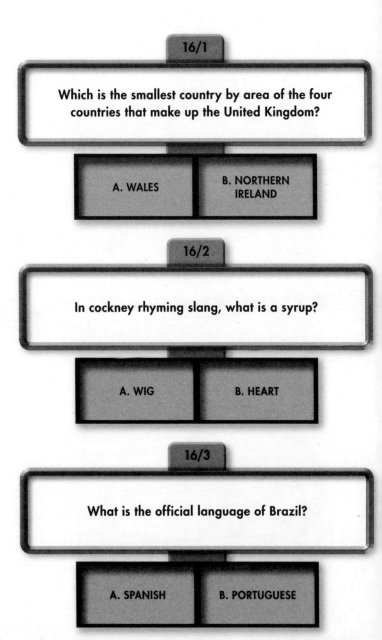

16/1

Which is the smallest country by area of the four countries that make up the United Kingdom?

A. WALES

B. NORTHERN IRELAND

16/2

In cockney rhyming slang, what is a syrup?

A. WIG

B. HEART

16/3

What is the official language of Brazil?

A. SPANISH

B. PORTUGUESE

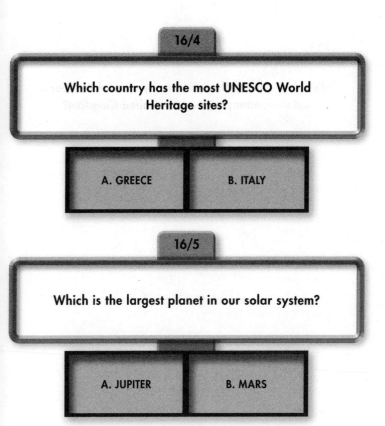

16/4

Which country has the most UNESCO World Heritage sites?

A. GREECE

B. ITALY

16/5

Which is the largest planet in our solar system?

A. JUPITER

B. MARS

QUESTIONS

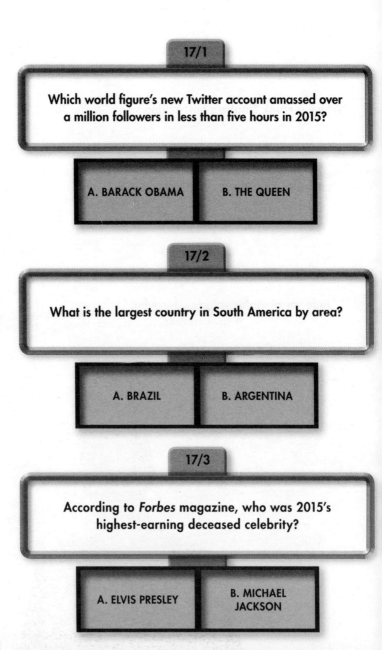

17/1

Which world figure's new Twitter account amassed over a million followers in less than five hours in 2015?

A. BARACK OBAMA

B. THE QUEEN

17/2

What is the largest country in South America by area?

A. BRAZIL

B. ARGENTINA

17/3

According to *Forbes* magazine, who was 2015's highest-earning deceased celebrity?

A. ELVIS PRESLEY

B. MICHAEL JACKSON

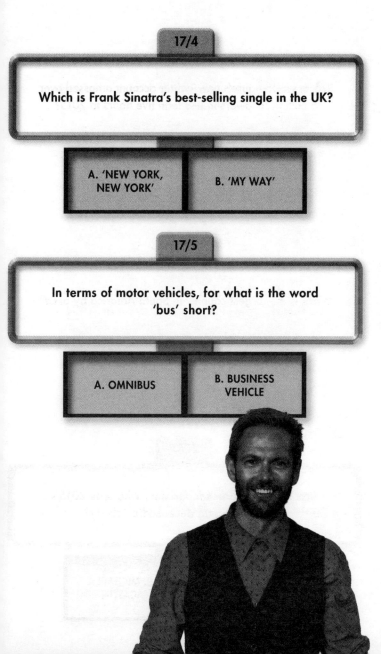

17/4

Which is Frank Sinatra's best-selling single in the UK?

A. 'NEW YORK, NEW YORK'

B. 'MY WAY'

17/5

In terms of motor vehicles, for what is the word 'bus' short?

A. OMNIBUS

B. BUSINESS VEHICLE

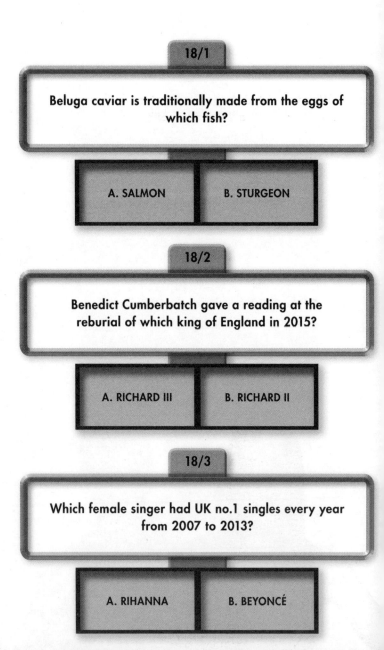

18/1

Beluga caviar is traditionally made from the eggs of which fish?

A. SALMON

B. STURGEON

18/2

Benedict Cumberbatch gave a reading at the reburial of which king of England in 2015?

A. RICHARD III

B. RICHARD II

18/3

Which female singer had UK no.1 singles every year from 2007 to 2013?

A. RIHANNA

B. BEYONCÉ

18/4

Who was voted the greatest Briton of all time in a 2002 BBC poll?

A. WINSTON CHURCHILL

B. DAVID BECKHAM

18/5

Of the 193 countries of the United Nations, the names of 26 begin with which letter?

A. B

B. S

QUESTIONS

215

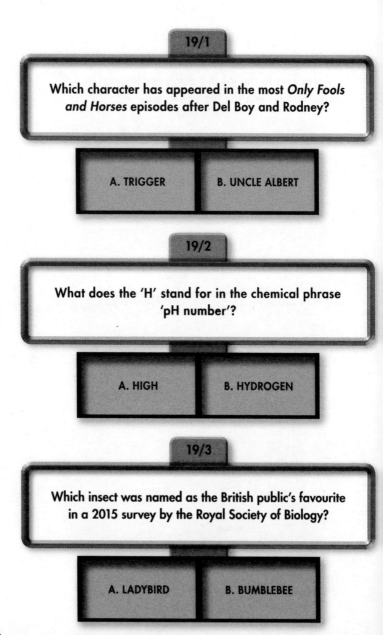

QUESTIONS

19/1

Which character has appeared in the most *Only Fools and Horses* episodes after Del Boy and Rodney?

A. TRIGGER

B. UNCLE ALBERT

19/2

What does the 'H' stand for in the chemical phrase 'pH number'?

A. HIGH

B. HYDROGEN

19/3

Which insect was named as the British public's favourite in a 2015 survey by the Royal Society of Biology?

A. LADYBIRD

B. BUMBLEBEE

19/4

According to the RAJAR audience figures, which radio station has the highest number of listeners in the UK?

| A. BBC RADIO 1 | B. BBC RADIO 2 |

19/5

In which country was the writer Rudyard Kipling born?

| A. INDIA | B. SOUTH AFRICA |

QUESTIONS

QUESTIONS

20/1

According to the RSPB, what is the UK's most widespread and common bird of prey?

A. BUZZARD

B. KESTREL

20/2

Who is the longest-reigning monarch in the history of the United Kingdom?

A. QUEEN VICTORIA

B. QUEEN ELIZABETH II

20/3

Which type of animal is the Warner Brothers character Pepé le Pew?

A. DOG

B. SKUNK

20/4

What did the USA purchase from Russia for $7.2 million in 1867?

A. CANADA

B. ALASKA

20/5

According to a 2016 YouGov poll, which celebrity is the most admired woman in the world?

A. ANGELINA JOLIE

B. BEYONCÉ

QUESTIONS

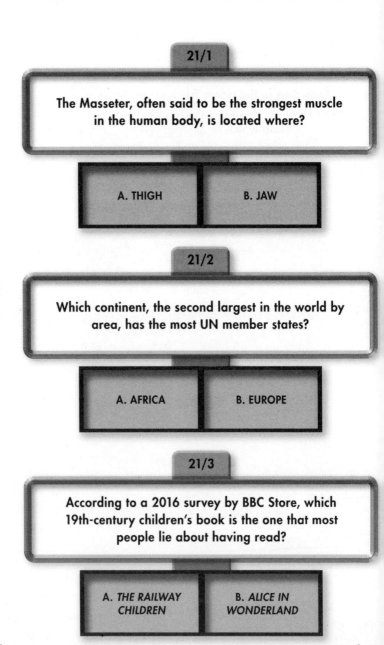

21/1

The Masseter, often said to be the strongest muscle in the human body, is located where?

A. THIGH

B. JAW

21/2

Which continent, the second largest in the world by area, has the most UN member states?

A. AFRICA

B. EUROPE

21/3

According to a 2016 survey by BBC Store, which 19th-century children's book is the one that most people lie about having read?

A. *THE RAILWAY CHILDREN*

B. *ALICE IN WONDERLAND*

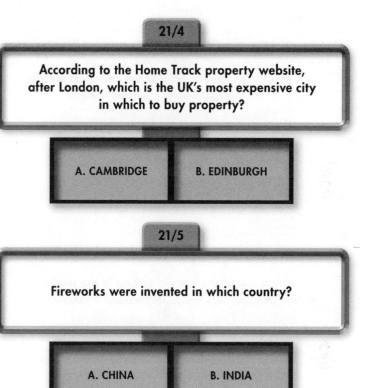

21/4

According to the Home Track property website, after London, which is the UK's most expensive city in which to buy property?

A. CAMBRIDGE

B. EDINBURGH

21/5

Fireworks were invented in which country?

A. CHINA

B. INDIA

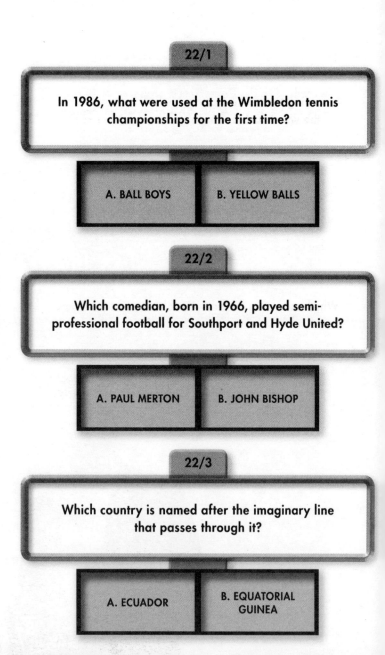

22/1

In 1986, what were used at the Wimbledon tennis championships for the first time?

A. BALL BOYS

B. YELLOW BALLS

22/2

Which comedian, born in 1966, played semi-professional football for Southport and Hyde United?

A. PAUL MERTON

B. JOHN BISHOP

22/3

Which country is named after the imaginary line that passes through it?

A. ECUADOR

B. EQUATORIAL GUINEA

22/4

According to a 2016 Harvey Nichols survey, what is the worst fashion mistake a man can make?

| A. SOCKS AND SANDALS | B. LYCRA |

22/5

Which man won his first Wimbledon Men's Singles competition in 1981?

| A. JOHN MCENROE | B. BJORN BORG |

QUESTIONS

223

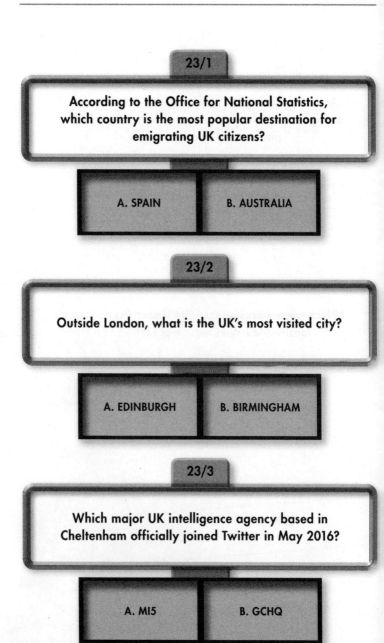

23/1

According to the Office for National Statistics, which country is the most popular destination for emigrating UK citizens?

A. SPAIN

B. AUSTRALIA

23/2

Outside London, what is the UK's most visited city?

A. EDINBURGH

B. BIRMINGHAM

23/3

Which major UK intelligence agency based in Cheltenham officially joined Twitter in May 2016?

A. MI5

B. GCHQ

23/4

According to a 2016 survey, which 90-year-old TV presenter was the person most people would like to have as a dinner party guest?

| A. SIR DAVID ATTENBOROUGH | B. SIR BRUCE FORSYTH |

23/5

Which former president of the United States has the most-edited Wikipedia page of all time?

| A. GEORGE W BUSH | B. BILL CLINTON |

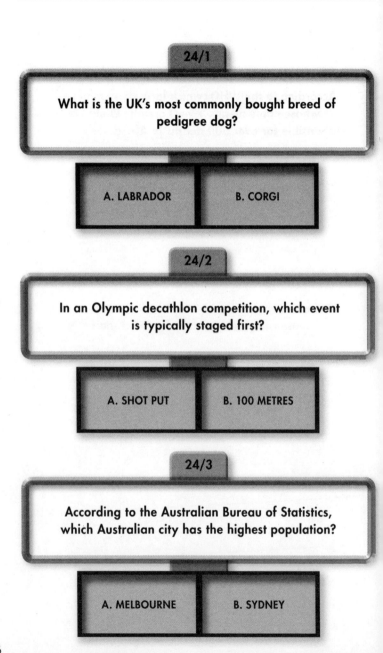

24/1

What is the UK's most commonly bought breed of pedigree dog?

A. LABRADOR

B. CORGI

24/2

In an Olympic decathlon competition, which event is typically staged first?

A. SHOT PUT

B. 100 METRES

24/3

According to the Australian Bureau of Statistics, which Australian city has the highest population?

A. MELBOURNE

B. SYDNEY

24/4

According to the WHO, which large land mammal, whose name means 'river horse' in Greek, is responsible for over 500 deaths in Africa every year?

| A. ELEPHANT | B. HIPPOPOTAMUS |

24/5

What is Britain's busiest train station in terms of passenger numbers?

| A. LONDON WATERLOO | B. LONDON KING'S CROSS |

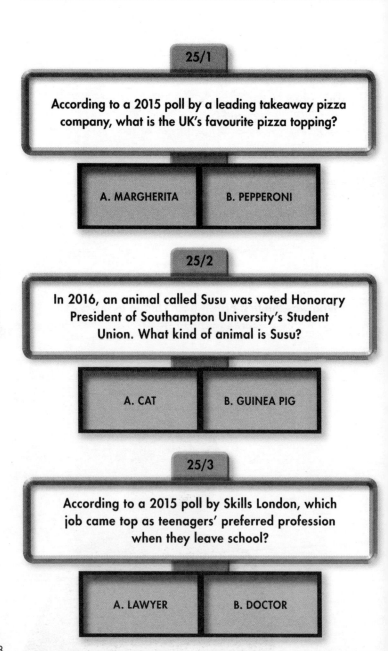

25/1

According to a 2015 poll by a leading takeaway pizza company, what is the UK's favourite pizza topping?

A. MARGHERITA   B. PEPPERONI

25/2

In 2016, an animal called Susu was voted Honorary President of Southampton University's Student Union. What kind of animal is Susu?

A. CAT   B. GUINEA PIG

25/3

According to a 2015 poll by Skills London, which job came top as teenagers' preferred profession when they leave school?

A. LAWYER   B. DOCTOR

QUESTIONS

25/4

Who is the shortest man to have played James Bond
in official feature films?

| A. ROGER MOORE | B. DANIEL CRAIG |

25/5

Who was the first British-born chef to be awarded
three Michelin stars?

| A. MARCO PIERRE WHITE | B. GORDON RAMSAY |

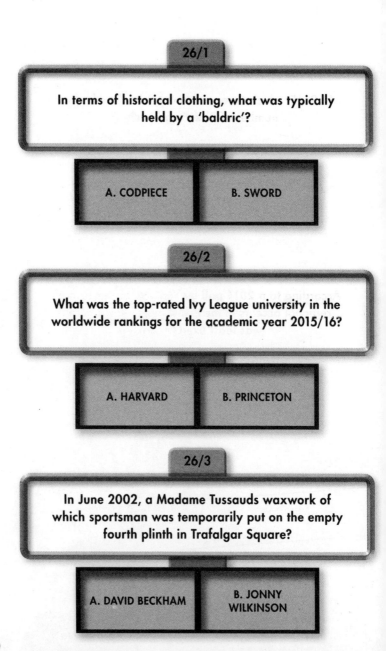

26/1

In terms of historical clothing, what was typically held by a 'baldric'?

A. CODPIECE

B. SWORD

26/2

What was the top-rated Ivy League university in the worldwide rankings for the academic year 2015/16?

A. HARVARD

B. PRINCETON

26/3

In June 2002, a Madame Tussauds waxwork of which sportsman was temporarily put on the empty fourth plinth in Trafalgar Square?

A. DAVID BECKHAM

B. JONNY WILKINSON

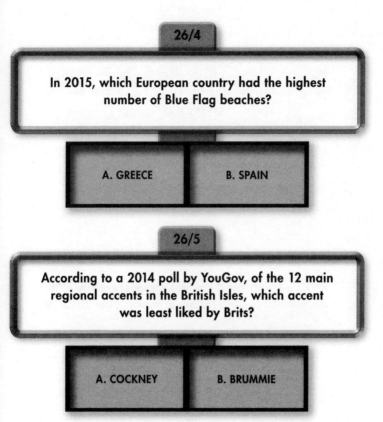

26/4

In 2015, which European country had the highest number of Blue Flag beaches?

| A. GREECE | B. SPAIN |

26/5

According to a 2014 poll by YouGov, of the 12 main regional accents in the British Isles, which accent was least liked by Brits?

| A. COCKNEY | B. BRUMMIE |

QUESTIONS

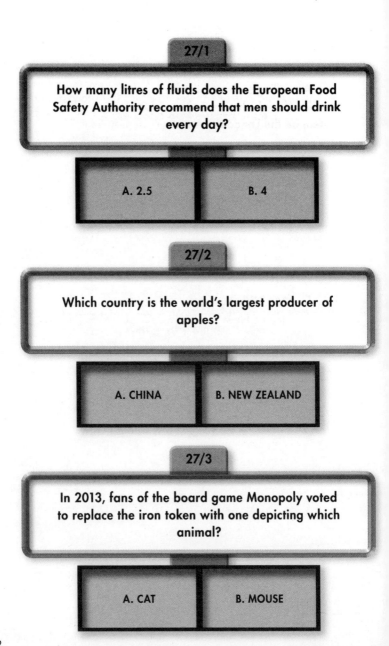

27/1

How many litres of fluids does the European Food Safety Authority recommend that men should drink every day?

A. 2.5

B. 4

27/2

Which country is the world's largest producer of apples?

A. CHINA

B. NEW ZEALAND

27/3

In 2013, fans of the board game Monopoly voted to replace the iron token with one depicting which animal?

A. CAT

B. MOUSE

QUESTIONS

27/4

According to Transport for London, after travelcards, which was the most commonly mislaid item on the London transport system in 2015?

A. UMBRELLAS

B. MOBILE PHONES

27/5

Number 350 Fifth Avenue is the address of which iconic New York City building?

A. EMPIRE STATE BUILDING

B. TRUMP TOWER

QUESTIONS

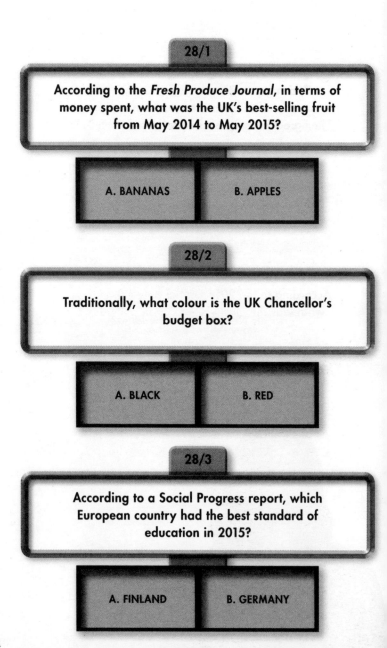

28/1

According to the *Fresh Produce Journal*, in terms of money spent, what was the UK's best-selling fruit from May 2014 to May 2015?

A. BANANAS

B. APPLES

28/2

Traditionally, what colour is the UK Chancellor's budget box?

A. BLACK

B. RED

28/3

According to a Social Progress report, which European country had the best standard of education in 2015?

A. FINLAND

B. GERMANY

28/4

Which gas, with the symbol CH4, is often considered to be the second most significant greenhouse gas after carbon dioxide?

| A. HELIUM | B. METHANE |

28/5

According to the 2014 Global Destination Index, what was the most visited city in the world by international visitors?

| A. NEW YORK | B. LONDON |

235

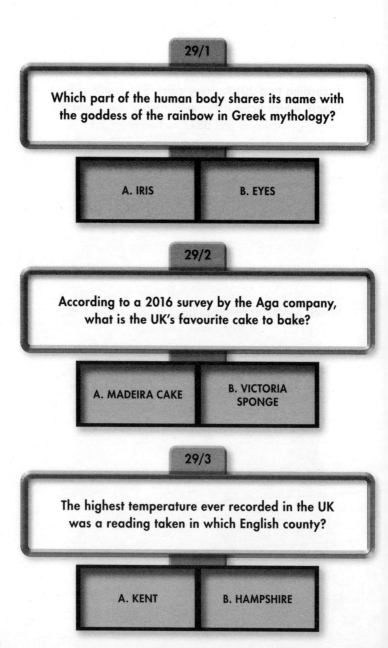

29/1

Which part of the human body shares its name with the goddess of the rainbow in Greek mythology?

A. IRIS

B. EYES

29/2

According to a 2016 survey by the Aga company, what is the UK's favourite cake to bake?

A. MADEIRA CAKE

B. VICTORIA SPONGE

29/3

The highest temperature ever recorded in the UK was a reading taken in which English county?

A. KENT

B. HAMPSHIRE

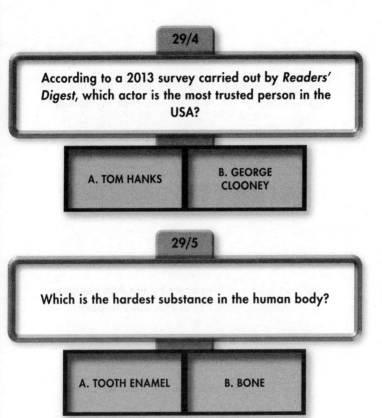

29/4

According to a 2013 survey carried out by *Readers' Digest*, which actor is the most trusted person in the USA?

A. TOM HANKS

B. GEORGE CLOONEY

29/5

Which is the hardest substance in the human body?

A. TOOTH ENAMEL

B. BONE

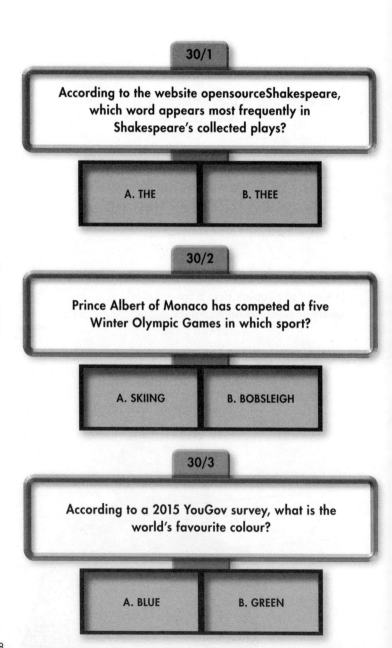

30/1

According to the website opensourceShakespeare, which word appears most frequently in Shakespeare's collected plays?

A. THE

B. THEE

30/2

Prince Albert of Monaco has competed at five Winter Olympic Games in which sport?

A. SKIING

B. BOBSLEIGH

30/3

According to a 2015 YouGov survey, what is the world's favourite colour?

A. BLUE

B. GREEN

30/4

In which part of the human body is the 'cupid's bow' located?

A. PELVIS   B. UPPER LIP

30/5

In terms of people's first languages, which is held to be the most commonly spoken mother tongue in the European Union?

A. FRENCH   B. GERMAN

THINK TANKERS' WORST ANSWERS

In *Peter Pan*, what is Captain Hook's first name?

Think Tanker: Captain

Correct Answer:
James

The name of which vegetable is also said to be a pet name Prince Philip has for the Queen?

Think Tanker: Potato

Correct Answer:
Cabbage

THINK TANKERS' WORST ANSWERS

Who is the chief protagonist of the short story entitled 'The Adventure of the Speckled Band'?

Think Tanker: The Tax Man

Correct Answer:
Sherlock Holmes

The Teenage Mutant Ninja Turtles' names are Donatello, Raphael, Leonardo and which other?

Think Tanker: DiCaprio

Correct Answer:
Michelangelo

QUESTION:
IMPOSSIBLE

1/1

Which football club are known as 'The Chairboys'?

1/2

Whose memoir is entitled *The Life and Loves of a He-Devil*?

1/3

In 1981, a song by which band became the first to be played on MTV?

1/4

Who was the first British woman to have five UK no.1 solo hit singles?

1/5

In 2004, Margaret Thatcher's son was implicated in a plot to overthrow the government of which African nation?

QUESTIONS

244

QUESTION: IMPOSSIBLE QUIZ 2

2/1

What are the two middle names of Princess Charlotte, born in May 2015?

2/2

The Tour de France-winning cyclist Chris Froome was born in which country?

2/3

Which young English actor was named as *GQ* magazine's best-dressed man for the second year running in 2016?

2/4

According to the famous rhyme that starts 'Monday's child is fair of face', the child born on which day 'works hard for a living'?

2/5

Who played the title role in the 2014 film *John Wick*?

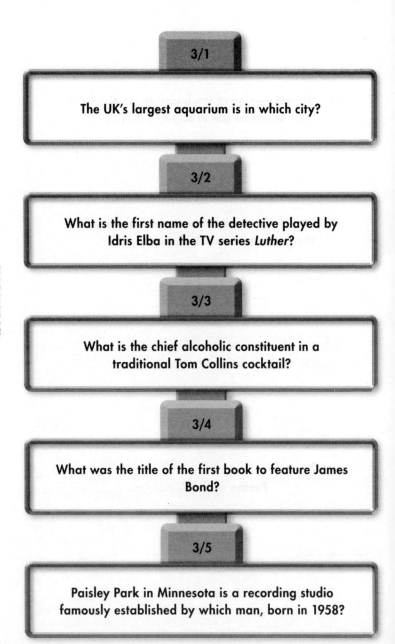

QUESTIONS

3/1

The UK's largest aquarium is in which city?

3/2

What is the first name of the detective played by Idris Elba in the TV series *Luther*?

3/3

What is the chief alcoholic constituent in a traditional Tom Collins cocktail?

3/4

What was the title of the first book to feature James Bond?

3/5

Paisley Park in Minnesota is a recording studio famously established by which man, born in 1958?

QUESTION: IMPOSSIBLE QUIZ 4

4/1

The original version of the board game Monopoly was based on the streets of which city?

4/2

The titles of how many Shakespeare plays include the names of two individual characters?

4/3

In 2015, who became the first footballer to score a goal in 11 consecutive Premier League matches?

4/4

In 1999, *Time* magazine named which man as their Person of the Century?

4/5

The cyclist Mark Cavendish was born on which island?

5/1

Which rugby league team has won the Challenge Cup on the most occasions?

5/2

Which male actor has been nominated for an Oscar in an acting category the most times?

5/3

In total, how many British kings and queens reigned during the 20th century?

5/4

What is the rarest colour for naturally occurring diamonds?

5/5

Which English town became a city as part of the Queen's Diamond Jubilee celebrations?

THINK TANKERS' WORST ANSWERS

The Briton Adam Peaty has won world titles in which sport?

Think Tanker:
Tiddlywinks

Correct Answer:
Swimming

Which famous children's book was written by Ian Fleming?

Think Tanker:
003½

Correct Answer:
Chitty Chitty Bang Bang

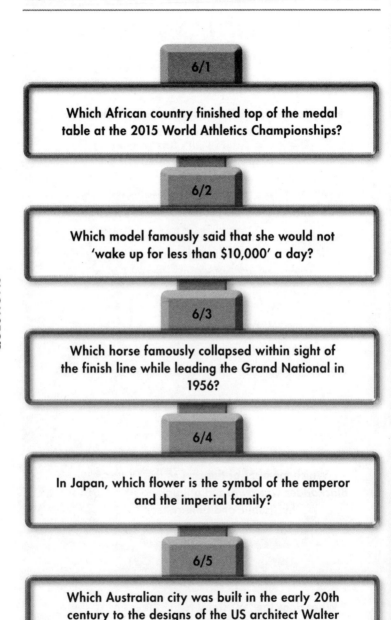

6/1

Which African country finished top of the medal table at the 2015 World Athletics Championships?

6/2

Which model famously said that she would not 'wake up for less than $10,000' a day?

6/3

Which horse famously collapsed within sight of the finish line while leading the Grand National in 1956?

6/4

In Japan, which flower is the symbol of the emperor and the imperial family?

6/5

Which Australian city was built in the early 20th century to the designs of the US architect Walter Burley Griffin?

QUESTION: IMPOSSIBLE QUIZ 7

7/1

'Hairy long-nosed', 'Nine-banded' and 'Pink Fairy' are varieties of which animal?

7/2

The word 'tonsorial' relates specifically to people in which line of work?

7/3

In 2012, who became Britain's most successful female Summer Olympian, with two golds and one silver?

7/4

Which member of the cast of the TV comedy *Blackadder* was awarded a knighthood in 2013 for his 'public and political service'?

7/5

What does the 'W' stand for in the name of the former US President George W Bush?

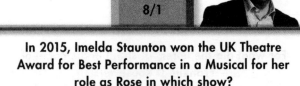

8/1

In 2015, Imelda Staunton won the UK Theatre Award for Best Performance in a Musical for her role as Rose in which show?

8/2

The racing driver Ayrton Senna was born in which country?

8/3

The word 'Mackem' refers to people from which city?

8/4

The Bank of England £10 note introduced in 2000 featured which man on the back?

8/5

For what does the 'GI' stand in terms of the 'GI diet'?

252

9/1

For what did the letter 'D' stand in the name of Franklin D Roosevelt?

9/2

Aorangi Terrace is a feature of which UK sporting venue?

9/3

Which actress was nominated for an Oscar in 2016 for her role in the British film *45 Years*?

9/4

In 1960, which country became the first to elect a female Prime Minister?

9/5

In *Downton Abbey*, what is the first name of the Countess of Grantham, played by Elizabeth McGovern?

253

QUESTIONS

10/1

In Indian cuisine, what vegetable is referred to as 'brinjal'?

10/2

Which former political leader once played a ghost in a Pakistani soap opera?

10/3

David Cameron became the MP for which constituency in 2001?

10/4

At the 2015 FIFA Women's World Cup, who captained the England team?

10/5

Which American football team won the 2016 Super Bowl?

THINK TANKERS' WORST ANSWERS

According to her modelling agency's official website, what is Kate Moss' waist size in inches?

Think Tanker:
6

Correct Answer:
26

Kevin, Bob and Stuart are the three main characters in which 2015 film?

Think Tanker:
The Kray Twins

Correct Answer:
Minions

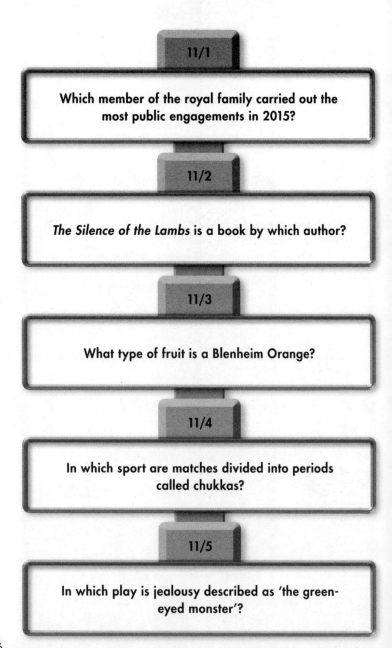

11/1

Which member of the royal family carried out the most public engagements in 2015?

11/2

The Silence of the Lambs is a book by which author?

11/3

What type of fruit is a Blenheim Orange?

11/4

In which sport are matches divided into periods called chukkas?

11/5

In which play is jealousy described as 'the green-eyed monster'?

QUESTION: IMPOSSIBLE QUIZ 12

12/1

Which type of pasta takes its name from the Italian word for 'butterfly'?

12/2

Which superhero was played by the British actor Tom Holland in the 2016 film *Captain America: Civil War*?

12/3

The TV sitcom *Mrs Brown's Boys* is set in which country?

12/4

In 2015, James Vince made his debut for England in which sport?

12/5

Ni is the chemical symbol of which element?

QUESTIONS

13/1

Donald Trump was born in which US state?

13/2

Which literary detective has an older brother named Mycroft?

13/3

'Can't Stop the Feeling' was a UK hit single for which singer in 2016?

13/4

Who played the role of Carrie in *Four Weddings and a Funeral*?

13/5

Who was sacked as the manager of Manchester United in May 2016?

14/1

The dish Wiener Schnitzel takes its name from that of which European capital city?

14/2

Which literary post did Carol Ann Duffy take up in 2009?

14/3

Who provides the voice for Dory in the films *Finding Nemo* and *Finding Dory*?

14/4

Which landlocked body of water to the east of the Caucasus mountains is often referred to as the largest lake in the world?

14/5

Which aviator made the first non-stop solo flight across the Atlantic Ocean, from New York City to Paris, in May 1927?

QUESTIONS

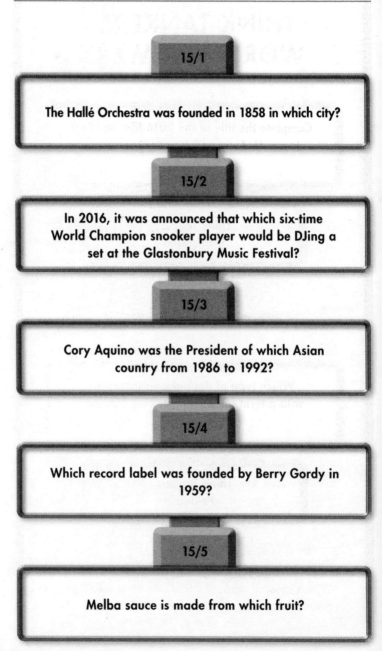

15/1

The Hallé Orchestra was founded in 1858 in which city?

15/2

In 2016, it was announced that which six-time World Champion snooker player would be DJing a set at the Glastonbury Music Festival?

15/3

Cory Aquino was the President of which Asian country from 1986 to 1992?

15/4

Which record label was founded by Berry Gordy in 1959?

15/5

Melba sauce is made from which fruit?

THINK TANKERS' WORST ANSWERS

Complete the title of the 2016 film starring James McAvoy and Jennifer Lawrence, *X-Men:...?*

Think Tanker:
Unplugged

Correct Answer:
Apocalypse

Which type of duck shares its name with a term for a high-ranking Chinese bureaucrat?

Think Tanker:
Peking

Correct Answer:
Mandarin

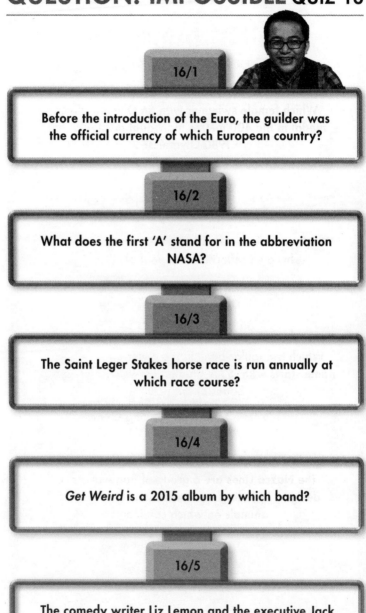

16/1

Before the introduction of the Euro, the guilder was the official currency of which European country?

16/2

What does the first 'A' stand for in the abbreviation NASA?

16/3

The Saint Leger Stakes horse race is run annually at which race course?

16/4

Get Weird is a 2015 album by which band?

16/5

The comedy writer Liz Lemon and the executive Jack Donaghy are characters in which TV comedy series?

QUESTION: IMPOSSIBLE QUIZ 17

17/1

Which female swimmer won an Olympic silver medal in the 400 metres individual medley at the 1980 Olympics?

17/2

Which youth from Greek mythology fell in love with his own reflection in a pool of water?

17/3

Which triangular bone in the lower back, whose name starts with 'S', is situated between the two hip bones of the pelvis?

17/4

The Nazca Lines are a group of huge abstract designs, including representations of birds and animals on which continent?

17/5

The Ring Cycle is a work by which composer?

QUESTIONS

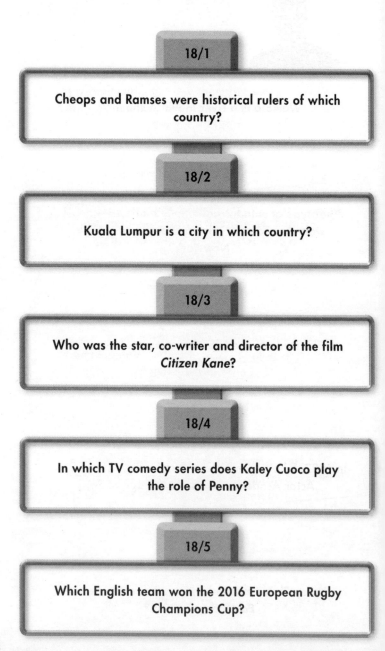

18/1

Cheops and Ramses were historical rulers of which country?

18/2

Kuala Lumpur is a city in which country?

18/3

Who was the star, co-writer and director of the film *Citizen Kane*?

18/4

In which TV comedy series does Kaley Cuoco play the role of Penny?

18/5

Which English team won the 2016 European Rugby Champions Cup?

QUESTION: IMPOSSIBLE QUIZ 19

19/1
Waikato is a river in which country?

19/2
What type of salad, traditionally made with apples, walnuts and celery, is named after a hotel in New York?

19/3
The Dodecanese Islands are a part of which country?

19/4
In 1982, who became the oldest man to win the Best Actor Academy Award, at the age of 76?

19/5
Stacey Slater married which other character in *EastEnders* in 2016?

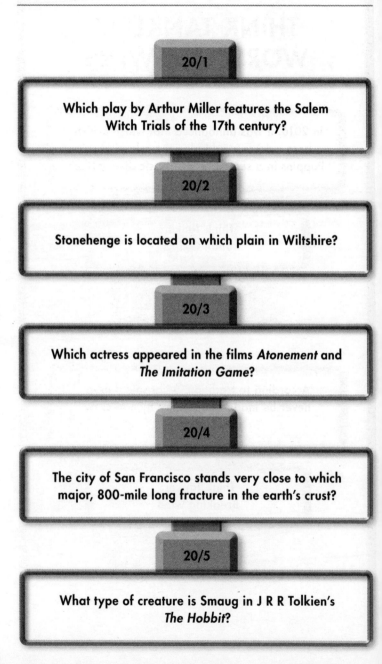

20/1

Which play by Arthur Miller features the Salem Witch Trials of the 17th century?

20/2

Stonehenge is located on which plain in Wiltshire?

20/3

Which actress appeared in the films *Atonement* and *The Imitation Game*?

20/4

The city of San Francisco stands very close to which major, 800-mile long fracture in the earth's crust?

20/5

What type of creature is Smaug in J R R Tolkien's *The Hobbit*?

THINK TANKERS' WORST ANSWERS

In 2016, it was announced that which British-born actress would play the role of Mary Poppins in a sequel to the classic Disney film?

Think Tanker:
Joan Collins

Correct Answer:
Emily Blunt

According to tradition, what sound must never be made in a theatre by non-crew members?

Think Tanker:
Breaking wind

Correct answer:
Whistle

21/1

The Australian actor Liam Hemsworth is famous for his engagement to which American singer and actress?

21/2

What type of food are 'porcini'?

21/3

The 1975 novel *Curtain* features the final case of which famous detective?

21/4

In which film did Sigourney Weaver play the zoologist Dian Fossey?

21/5

What was the nickname of the Anglo-Saxon king of England Ethelred II?

22/1

Which character from classical mythology had to perform 12 tasks to atone for his sins?

22/2

Which major river flows through Budapest?

22/3

What type of gemstone is the Koh-i-Noor?

22/4

Which language was created by Ludwig Zamenhof in the 19th century?

22/5

Which historic city was built on and around seven hills with names such as Palatine and Aventine?

QUESTIONS

269

23/1

Podgorica is the administrative capital of which European country whose name starts with 'M'?

23/2

The actor F Murray Abraham won an Oscar for his portrayal of the composer Antonio Salieri in which film of the 1980s?

23/3

Which is the largest castle in Wales?

23/4

Which Irish actor appeared in the films *In Bruges* and *Minority Report*?

23/5

Which birthday did the Queen celebrate in 2016?

QUESTION: IMPOSSIBLE QUIZ 24

24/1

Which football club lost to Sevilla in the final of the Europa League in 2016?

24/2

Who played the role of Richard III in the BBC TV drama series *The Hollow Crown: Wars of the Roses*?

24/3

What name, beginning with 'F', is given to the shanty towns or slum areas of Brazil?

24/4

Which Dutch tennis player won the Men's Singles Wimbledon title in 1996?

24/5

Kevin Federline is the ex-husband of which singer?

25/1

What was the first name of the man who founded the Porsche car company in 1931?

25/2

The UK had a series of so-called Cod Wars in 1970s with which island country?

25/3

A Game of Thrones is a book by which author?

25/4

The Klingons were characters in which TV series, first shown in 1966?

25/5

Which literary character was famously said to be 'tilting at windmills' – believing them to be giant knights?

THINK TANKERS' WORST ANSWERS

According to a famous quote by Samuel Johnson, someone is 'tired of life' when they are tired of which city?

Think Tanker:
Las Vegas

Correct Answer:
London

The letter 'L' on a car registration plate means it comes from which country?

Think Tanker:
Germany

Correct Answer:
Luxembourg

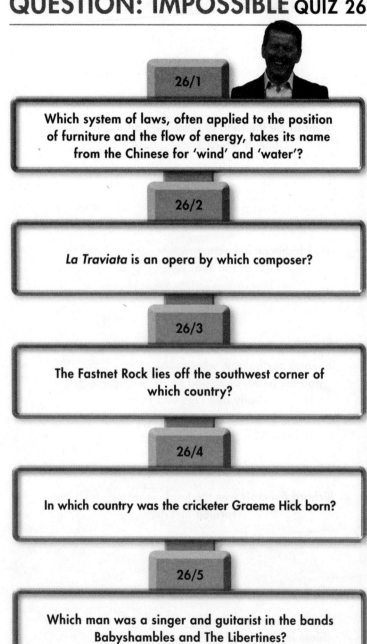

26/1

Which system of laws, often applied to the position of furniture and the flow of energy, takes its name from the Chinese for 'wind' and 'water'?

26/2

La Traviata is an opera by which composer?

26/3

The Fastnet Rock lies off the southwest corner of which country?

26/4

In which country was the cricketer Graeme Hick born?

26/5

Which man was a singer and guitarist in the bands Babyshambles and The Libertines?

QUESTION: IMPOSSIBLE QUIZ 27

27/1

'If music be the food of love, play on' is the opening line of which Shakespeare play?

27/2

Which diminutive actor was the male winner of the Rear of the Year Award in 2015?

27/3

In Greek mythology, what creature was Chiron, who had the head, arms and torso of a man and the body and legs of a horse?

27/4

Richard Ashcroft was the lead singer of which band formed in 1989?

27/5

Which international rugby union team won a Grand Slam in the mens' 2016 Six Nations tournament?

28/1

Ian Fleming's fictional spy James Bond was 'removed' from which famous school after an alleged incident with one of the Boys' Maids?

28/2

Windhoek is the capital of which country?

28/3

What type of motor vehicle with living accommodation is named after a native American tribe from Wisconsin?

28/4

Rooney Mara and Cate Blanchett received Oscar nominations for their roles in which 2015 film?

28/5

Views is a 2016 album by which rapper?

THINK TANKERS'
WORST ANSWERS

When the famous 'Hollywood' sign was first erected in 1923, what word did it display?

Think Tanker:
Hi

Correct Answer:
Hollywoodland

What does a lepidopterist study?

Think Tanker:
Fat feet

Correct Answer:
Butterflies

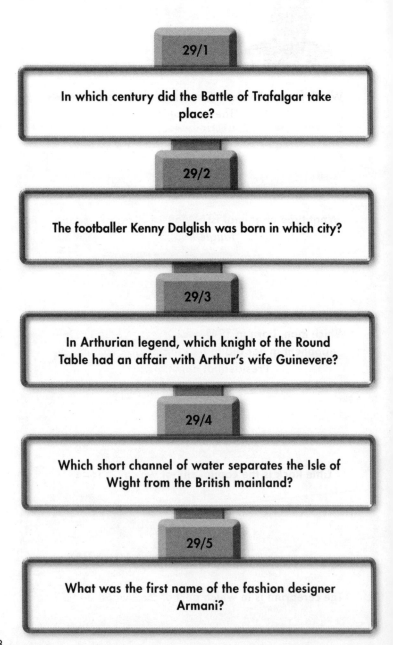

29/1

In which century did the Battle of Trafalgar take place?

29/2

The footballer Kenny Dalglish was born in which city?

29/3

In Arthurian legend, which knight of the Round Table had an affair with Arthur's wife Guinevere?

29/4

Which short channel of water separates the Isle of Wight from the British mainland?

29/5

What was the first name of the fashion designer Armani?

30/1

Which former Formula One Champion is nicknamed 'The Ice Man'?

30/2

What type of animal is Akela in Rudyard Kipling's *Jungle Book*?

30/3

Which man, born in 1941, was Hillary Clinton's chief opponent in her bid to be the Democratic Party's Presidential nomination?

30/4

Little Rock is the capital city of which US state?

30/5

The cerebrum is in which part of the human body?

QUESTIONS

THINK TANKERS' WORST ANSWERS

The 2016 stage play based on a story by J K Rowling, Jack Thorne and John Tiffany is titled *Harry Potter and the...* what?

Think Tanker: Big Stage

Correct Answer:
Cursed Child

'Mantequilla' is the Spanish word for which food?

Think Tanker: Paella

Correct Answer:
Butter

THINK TANKERS' WORST ANSWERS

By what name is the fashion blogger Zoe Sugg better known by online fans?

Think Tanker: The Sugg-Meister

Correct Answer: Zoella

The so-called statue of Eros in London's Piccadilly Circus was one of the first in the capital to be cast in which metal?

Think Tanker: Gold

Correct Answer: Aluminium

ANSWERS

ANSWERS

ROUND 1

QUIZ 1:

1/1 Cilla Black
1/2 Novak Djokovic
1/3 Alaska
1/4 Web Log
1/5 Fox
1/6 Angela Merkel

QUIZ 2:

2/1 Paul Young
2/2 DeLorean
2/3 Beaver
2/4 Duke
2/5 Alan Bennett
2/6 Motörhead

QUIZ 3:

3/1 Liver
3/2 Tarzan
3/3 Suffolk
3/4 Plum
3/5 People
3/6 4

QUIZ 4:

4/1 Elton John
4/2 Saint
4/3 Bray
4/4 Andre Agassi
4/5 Horses
4/6 Father Christmas

QUIZ 5:

5/1 Melon
5/2 Sam Smith
5/3 Oscar Wilde
5/4 Orangutan
5/5 Hat
5/6 Gauguin

QUIZ 6:

6/1 Beagle
6/2 Virginia Wade
6/3 Smokey Robinson
6/4 Bear Grylls
6/5 Nelson Mandela
6/6 BBC

QUIZ 7:

7/1 3
7/2 Elbow
7/3 Umbrella
7/4 Louis Walsh
7/5 Thank you
7/6 Michael Heseltine

QUIZ 8:

8/1 Chris Robshaw
8/2 Liverpool
8/3 Marvin Gaye
8/4 E L James
8/5 Sheffield
8/6 *The Walking Dead*

QUIZ 9:

9/1 Four
9/2 Crocus
9/3 New Zealand
9/4 James Bond
9/5 Blackpool
9/6 *Macbeth*

QUIZ 10:

10/1 *Mastermind*
10/2 The Gruffalo
10/3 Johnny Depp
10/4 South America
10/5 Richard Nixon
10/6 Neck

QUIZ 11:

11/1 Meteorite
11/2 *Dirty Dancing*
11/3 Seattle
11/4 Billy the Kid
11/5 Driver
11/6 Peter

QUIZ 12:

12/1 Oxford
12/2 *The Thick of It*
12/3 Bear Grylls
12/4 Gorgon
12/5 Brazil
12/6 Shayne Ward

QUIZ 13:

13/1 Scientology
13/2 Lead
13/3 Nicolas Cage
13/4 China
13/5 Ministry
13/6 *Hair*

QUIZ 14:

14/1 Triceratops
14/2 Belgium
14/3 Cycling
14/4 Buenos Aires
14/5 Alec Guinness
14/6 Hawaii

QUIZ 15:

15/1 Calvin Harris
15/2 Leeds
15/3 Konnie Huq
15/4 *The Artist*
15/5 Winston Churchill
15/6 Lima

ANSWERS

ROUND 1

QUIZ 16:

16/1 Sweden

16/2 Margaret

16/3 Joanne

16/4 Denmark

16/5 Corgi

16/6 Notre Dame

QUIZ 17:

17/1 Adelaide

17/2 Fedora

17/3 Noël Coward

17/4 New York

17/5 Sean Penn

17/6 Steven

QUIZ 18:

18/1 Jonathan Ross

18/2 Panda

18/3 Hugh Laurie

18/4 Baku

18/5 Moustache

18/6 Chickpeas

QUIZ 19:

19/1 Winston Churchill

19/2 Istanbul

19/3 Seven

19/4 Soup Dragons

19/5 Sagittarius

19/6 Italy

QUIZ 20:

20/1 Umbrella

20/2 Horse

20/3 Melania

20/4 Badminton

20/5 West Ham United

20/6 Ears

QUIZ 21:

21/1 Doctor

21/2 Victoria Beckham

21/3 Winston Churchill

21/4 Sheena Easton

21/5 Rick Astley

21/6 Australia

QUIZ 22:

22/1 Joe Biden

22/2 *Quantum of Solace*

22/3 3

22/4 Flash Gordon

22/5 Papaya

22/6 Australia

QUIZ 23:

23/1 Prince Edward

23/2 David Bowie

23/3 Cockerel

23/4 *Spotlight*

23/5 32

23/6 Prince

QUIZ 24:

24/1 Cricket

24/2 Oxford

24/3 Switzerland

24/4 Star Wars

24/5 Blue

24/6 Mark Selby

QUIZ 25:

25/1 Brotherhood of Man

25/2 £70

25/3 Athens

25/4 California

25/5 X

25/6 Portugal

QUIZ 26:

26/1 Ken Dodd

26/2 Swansea City

26/3 Puffin

26/4 Sperm whale

26/5 Robert De Niro

26/6 Malvern Hills

QUIZ 27:

27/1 Noah

27/2 Carbon

27/3 Baltimore

27/4 Isle of Man

27/5 *Oliver Twist*

27/6 Switzerland

QUIZ 28:

28/1 Foxes

28/2 Polish

28/3 Graham Chapman

28/4 Winston

28/5 Bologna

28/6 George Foreman

QUIZ 29:

29/1 *Grey's Anatomy*

29/2 Nipples

29/3 Mis-Teeq

29/4 Rolls-Royce

29/5 Woodpecker

29/6 81

QUIZ 30:

30/1 Steve Brookstein

30/2 Thursday

30/3 Warhol

30/4 Rebecca

30/5 Orkney Islands

30/6 Drake

ANSWERS

ROUND 2

QUIZ 1:

1/1 Barista
1/2 Reindeer
1/3 Sarah Lancashire
1/4 *Dodgeball: A True Underdog Story*
1/5 Humour
1/6 'Copacabana'
1/7 Mexico
1/8 Thierry Henry
1/9 Grace Jones

QUIZ 2:

2/1 Carbon dioxide
2/2 Ant-Man
2/3 Diversity
2/4 *Brighton Rock*
2/5 Black
2/6 Cod
2/7 Tottenham Hotspur
2/8 'Chasing Pavements'
2/9 Turkey

QUIZ 3:

3/1 New Zealand
3/2 Table Mountain
3/3 Red and white
3/4 Quahog
3/5 Barcelona
3/6 Penny Black
3/7 Indonesia
3/8 Warwickshire
3/9 Soup

QUIZ 4:

4/1 Wayne Gretzky
4/2 Alan Ayckbourn
4/3 Rik Mayall
4/4 I
4/5 Leicester City
4/6 Amy
4/7 *There's Something About Mary*
4/8 Charleston
4/9 The Football Association

QUIZ 5:

5/1 Bridgetown
5/2 *My Fair Lady*
5/3 U2
5/4 The Derby
5/5 Soya beans
5/6 Mexico
5/7 Gwen Stefani
5/8 Beagle
5/9 *Coronation Street*

QUIZ 6:

6/1 Saturday
6/2 Tutankhamun
6/3 Kidneys
6/4 Pauline Collins
6/5 Spain
6/6 Bucket
6/7 Tungsten
6/8 Aretha Franklin
6/9 René Descartes

QUIZ 7:

7/1	Sonic The Hedgehog
7/2	*The Ladykillers*
7/3	Blenheim Palace
7/4	Ottawa
7/5	Lucy Beale
7/6	Albrecht Dürer
7/7	Basketball
7/8	Usbourne
7/9	Billie Piper

QUIZ 8:

8/1	Austria
8/2	Corporal
8/3	Edinburgh
8/4	Liverpool FC
8/5	Sodor
8/6	German measles
8/7	D:Ream
8/8	*The Big Bang Theory*
8/9	Mañana

QUIZ 9:

9/1	Marlon Brando
9/2	Humbug
9/3	Mahalia Jackson
9/4	Sandhurst
9/5	Trevor McDonald
9/6	Switzerland
9/7	Barcelona
9/8	Peter Falk
9/9	*The Revenant*

QUIZ 10:

10/1	Harold Wilson
10/2	Seattle
10/3	Quebec
10/4	Usher
10/5	Blue
10/6	Knitting
10/7	Christopher Lee
10/8	Bobby Beale
10/9	Manhattan

QUIZ 11:

11/1	Electrocardiogram
11/2	Jamaica
11/3	Egypt
11/4	Costa Brava
11/5	Ferret
11/6	Pineapple
11/7	*The Last Battle*
11/8	Al Green
11/9	Asia

ANSWERS

ROUND 2

QUIZ 12:

12/1 Balearic Islands
12/2 Washington DC
12/3 Calais
12/4 Jerez
12/5 Aneurin Bevan
12/6 South Africa
12/7 Clive Lloyd
12/8 Dave Lamb
12/9 Richard Branson

QUIZ 13:

13/1 Colin Jackson
13/2 Burrito
13/3 Clint Eastwood
13/4 New Orleans
13/5 Margherita
13/6 *Baby*
13/7 Iwan Thomas
13/8 Ukraine
13/9 *The Blind Side*

QUIZ 14:

14/1 Farrow
14/2 *Geordie Shore*
14/3 Atlantic Ocean
14/4 Ireland
14/5 R L Stine
14/6 Latvia
14/7 Red
14/8 Nigella Lawson
14/9 Wales

QUIZ 15:

15/1 The sun
15/2 Pancreas
15/3 Handel
15/4 Luigi
15/5 *The Thin Blue Line*
15/6 X-Men
15/7 Rio de Janeiro
15/8 *Ray*
15/9 Waterloo

QUIZ 16:

16/1 Kneecap
16/2 Rugby union
16/3 A jump
16/4 Canada
16/5 Legs
16/6 Lake Garda
16/7 Suranne Jones
16/8 Edgar Wright
16/9 Joe Pesci

QUIZ 17:

17/1 Nana
17/2 Kirsty Young
17/3 Lewis Carroll
17/4 James Corden
17/5 Martin Johnson
17/6 Denmark and Sweden
17/7 Lobster
17/8 Corfu
17/9 Mercury

QUIZ 18:

18/1 Apples

18/2 Harry Secombe

18/3 Sydney Opera House

18/4 'At Last'

18/5 *The Apprentice*

18/6 *Empire*

18/7 Madrid

18/8 Seth MacFarlane

18/9 Friend

QUIZ 19:

19/1 Wes Craven

19/2 *The Mikado*

19/3 'Goldfinger'

19/4 Hippocrates

19/5 'Space Oddity'

19/6 The Specials

19/7 Japan

19/8 John F Kennedy

19/9 Calcium

QUIZ 20:

20/1 *Breaking Bad*

20/2 Fidel Castro

20/3 *Good Will Hunting*

20/4 St Petersburg

20/5 Gymnastics

20/6 Taylor Lautner

20/7 Hugh Laurie

20/8 AC/DC

20/9 High

QUIZ 21:

21/1 Cormac McCarthy

21/2 Long jump

21/3 Voldemort

21/4 The Sistine Chapel

21/5 Serena Williams

21/6 Profumo

21/7 Indian Ocean

21/8 Mexico

21/9 Alma mater

ANSWERS

ROUND 2

QUIZ 22:

22/1 Blackbeard

22/2 Cara Delevingne

22/3 Waltz

22/4 Water

22/5 A smoked fish

22/6 Matt Damon

22/7 Pevensie

22/8 Shark

22/9 Italy

QUIZ 23:

23/1 Timpani

23/2 Eminem

23/3 German

23/4 United

23/5 Rita Ora

23/6 Philadelphia

23/7 Alfred

23/8 Danielle Steel

23/9 James Corden

QUIZ 24:

24/1 Density

24/2 Bald eagle

24/3 Nepal

24/4 Jeffrey Archer

24/5 Ashley Madison

24/6 10,000 metres

24/7 *What's Going On*

24/8 South America

24/9 *Elf*

QUIZ 25:

25/1 Quentin Tarantino

25/2 Scrabble

25/3 Tom Hardy

25/4 *Orange Is The New Black*

25/5 Mallorca

25/6 *Back to the Future*

25/7 David Schwimmer

25/8 Trinidad and Tobago

25/9 'Baker Street'

QUIZ 26:

26/1 Verruca

26/2 The Kabin

26/3 Stratford-upon-Avon

26/4 22

26/5 Ballet

26/6 New York

26/7 *Popcorn*

26/8 Northern Territory

26/9 Six

QUIZ 27:

27/1 Ike

27/2 Greenwich Park

27/3 *Hamlet*

27/4 Steps

27/5 Inverness

27/6 Red

27/7 Bruce Forsyth

27/8 23

27/9 Percussion

ANSWERS

QUIZ 28:

28/1 Igneous
28/2 The Boss
28/3 Tempura
28/4 Tom Ford
28/5 Rhodes
28/6 John Grisham
28/7 Dalmation
28/8 400
28/9 St Paul's Cathedral

QUIZ 29:

29/1 Kidney
29/2 The Queen
29/3 Seas
29/4 William Shakespeare
29/5 April
29/6 300
29/7 Niall Horan
29/8 Swansea
29/9 Windermere

QUIZ 30:

30/1 *Cheers*
30/2 Attila
30/3 *The Naked Chef*
30/4 Calzone
30/5 Christian Dior
30/6 Neon
30/7 Rocking horse
30/8 Four
30/9 Emperor

ANSWERS

ROUND 3

QUIZ 1:
1/1 Mosquito
1/2 Rugby Union World Cup
1/3 Czech Republic
1/4 Phil Mitchell
1/5 Robert Burns

QUIZ 2:
2/1 *Great British Bake Off*
2/2 Brussels
2/3 Mallorca
2/4 Barack Obama
2/5 Tails

QUIZ 3:
3/1 Google
3/2 An island
3/3 Dubai
3/4 White
3/5 Glastonbury Festival

QUIZ 4:
4/1 Basketball
4/2 Gordon Brown
4/3 Monopoly
4/4 China
4/5 Darren Gough

QUIZ 5:
5/1 Roger Moore
5/2 Bees
5/3 Prince Charles
5/4 Doctor
5/5 Australia

QUIZ 6:
6/1 Celtic
6/2 Jonathan Ross
6/3 Dogs
6/4 High Street
6/5 USA

QUIZ 7:
7/1 Africa
7/2 *The Archers*
7/3 France
7/4 Femur
7/5 South America

QUIZ 8:
8/1 *Les Misérables*
8/2 Johnny Depp
8/3 Robin
8/4 Tony Blair
8/5 Athletics

QUIZ 9:

9/1 Vladimir Putin
9/2 Rory McIlroy
9/3 Prince Harry
9/4 *The Queen's Christmas Message*
9/5 David Walliams

QUIZ 10:

10/1 Blackburn Rovers
10/2 Apple
10/3 Georgia
10/4 Red Sea
10/5 Ellie Goulding

QUIZ 11:

11/1 New York
11/2 'Holiday'
11/3 USA
11/4 *Daily Mail*
11/5 Spruce

QUIZ 12:

12/1 'What Makes You Beautiful'
12/2 1p
12/3 The Queen
12/4 Isle of Wight
12/5 Monaco

QUIZ 13:

13/1 Floyd Mayweather
13/2 Dog
13/3 *Breaking Bad*
13/4 Jolly Roger
13/5 Adele

QUIZ 14:

14/1 Bananas
14/2 Kendall Jenner
14/3 Vermont
14/4 *Star Wars: The Force Awakens*
14/5 Six

QUIZ 15:

15/1 California
15/2 Jarvis Cocker
15/3 Snow
15/4 Gisele Bündchen
15/5 Meryl Streep

QUIZ 16:

16/1 Northern Ireland
16/2 Wig
16/3 Portuguese
16/4 Italy
16/5 Jupiter

ANSWERS

ROUND 3

QUIZ 17:

17/1 Barack Obama

17/2 Brazil

17/3 Michael Jackson

17/4 'My Way'

17/5 Omnibus

QUIZ 18:

18/1 Sturgeon

18/2 Richard III

18/3 Rihanna

18/4 Winston Churchill

18/5 S

QUIZ 19:

19/1 Trigger

19/2 Hydrogen

19/3 Bumblebee

19/4 BBC Radio 2

19/5 India

QUIZ 20:

20/1 Buzzard

20/2 Queen Elizabeth II

20/3 Skunk

20/4 Alaska

20/5 Angelina Jolie

QUIZ 21:

21/1 Jaw

21/2 Africa

21/3 *Alice's Adventures in Wonderland*

21/4 Cambridge

21/5 China

QUIZ 22:

22/1 Yellow balls

22/2 John Bishop

22/3 Ecuador

22/4 Socks and sandals

22/5 John McEnroe

QUIZ 23:

23/1 Australia

23/2 Edinburgh

23/3 GCHQ

23/4 Sir David Attenborough

23/5 George W Bush

QUIZ 24:

24/1 Labrador

24/2 100 metres

24/3 Sydney

24/4 Hippopotamus

24/5 London Waterloo

QUIZ 25:
25/1 Pepperoni
25/2 Cat
25/3 Doctor
25/4 Daniel Craig
25/5 Marco Pierre White

QUIZ 26:
26/1 Sword
26/2 Harvard
26/3 David Beckham
26/4 Spain
26/5 Brummie

QUIZ 27:
27/1 2.5
27/2 China
27/3 Cat
27/4 Mobile phones
27/5 Empire State Building

QUIZ 28:
28/1 Apples
28/2 Red
28/3 Finland
28/4 Methane
28/5 London

QUIZ 29:
29/1 Iris
29/2 Victoria sponge
29/3 Kent
29/4 Tom Hanks
29/5 Tooth enamel

QUIZ 30:
30/1 The
30/2 Bobsleigh
30/3 Blue
30/4 Upper lip
30/5 German

ANSWERS

QUESTION IMPOSSIBLE

QUIZ 1:

1/1 Wycombe Wanderers

1/2 Graham Norton

1/3 The Buggles

1/4 Cheryl Fernandez-Versini

1/5 Equatorial Guinea

QUIZ 2:

2/1 Elizabeth Diana

2/2 Kenya

2/3 Eddie Redmayne

2/4 Saturday

2/5 Keanu Reeves

QUIZ 3:

3/1 Plymouth

3/2 John

3/3 Gin

3/4 *Casino Royale*

3/5 Prince

QUIZ 4:

4/1 Atlantic City

4/2 Three

4/3 Jamie Vardy

4/4 Albert Einstein

4/5 Isle of Man

QUIZ 5:

5/1 Wigan Warriors

5/2 Jack Nicholson

5/3 Six

5/4 Red

5/5 Chelmsford

QUIZ 6:

6/1 Kenya

6/2 Linda Evangelista

6/3 Devon Loch

6/4 Chrysanthemum

6/5 Canberra

QUIZ 7:

7/1 Armadillo

7/2 Hairdressing/barbers

7/3 Victoria Pendleton

7/4 Tony Robinson

7/5 Walker

QUIZ 8:

8/1 *Gypsy*

8/2 Brazil

8/3 Sunderland

8/4 Charles Darwin

8/5 Glycaemic Index

ANSWERS

QUIZ 9:

9/1   Delano

9/2   Wimbledon

9/3   Charlotte Rampling

9/4   Sri Lanka

9/5   Cora

QUIZ 10:

10/1   Aubergine

10/2   Alex Salmond

10/3   Witney

10/4   Steph Houghton

10/5   Denver Broncos

QUIZ 11:

11/1   Princess Anne

11/2   Thomas Harris

11/3   Apple

11/4   Polo

11/5   *Othello*

QUIZ 12:

12/1   Farfalle

12/2   Spider-Man

12/3   Ireland

12/4   Cricket

12/5   Nickel

QUIZ 13:

13/1   New York State

13/2   Sherlock Holmes

13/3   Justin Timberlake

13/4   Andie MacDowell

13/5   Louis van Gaal

QUIZ 14:

14/1   Vienna

14/2   Poet Laureate

14/3   Ellen Degeneres

14/4   Caspian Sea

14/5   Charles Lindbergh

QUIZ 15:

15/1   Manchester

15/2   Steve Davis

15/3   Philippines

15/4   Motown

15/5   Raspberries

QUIZ 16:

16/1   Netherlands

16/2   Aeronautics

16/3   Doncaster

16/4   Little Mix

16/5   *30 Rock*

ANSWERS

QUESTION IMPOSSIBLE

QUIZ 17:
17/1 Sharron Davies
17/2 Narcissus
17/3 Sacrum
17/4 South America
17/5 Richard Wagner

QUIZ 18:
18/1 Egypt
18/2 Malaysia
18/3 Orson Welles
18/4 The Big Bang Theory
18/5 Saracens

QUIZ 19:
19/1 New Zealand
19/2 Waldorf salad
19/3 Greece
19/4 Henry Fonda
19/5 Martin Fowler

QUIZ 20:
20/1 *The Crucible*
20/2 Salisbury Plain
20/3 Keira Knightley
20/4 San Andreas Fault
20/5 Dragon

QUIZ 21:
21/1 Miley Cyrus
21/2 Mushrooms
21/3 Hercule Poirot
21/4 *Gorillas in the Mist*
21/5 The Unready

QUIZ 22:
22/1 Heracles (Hercules)
22/2 Danube
22/3 Diamond
22/4 Esperanto
22/5 Rome

QUIZ 23:
23/1 Montenegro
23/2 *Amadeus*
23/3 Caerphilly Castle
23/4 Colin Farrell
23/5 90th

QUIZ 24:
24/1 Liverpool
24/2 Benedict Cumberbatch
24/3 Favela
24/4 Richard Krajicek
24/5 Britney Spears

QUIZ 25:

25/1 Ferdinand
25/2 Iceland
25/3 George R R Martin
25/4 *Star Trek*
25/5 Don Quixote

QUIZ 26:

26/1 Feng shui
26/2 Verdi
26/3 Ireland
26/4 Zimbabwe (Rhodesia)
26/5 Pete Doherty

QUIZ 27:

27/1 *Twelfth Night*
27/2 Daniel Radcliffe
27/3 Centaur
27/4 The Verve
27/5 England

QUIZ 28:

28/1 Eton College
28/2 Namibia
28/3 Winnebago
28/4 *Carol*
28/5 Drake

QUIZ 29:

29/1 19th
29/2 Glasgow
29/3 Lancelot
29/4 Solent
29/5 Giorgio

QUIZ 30:

30/1 Kimi Raikkonen
30/2 Wolf
30/3 Bernie Sanders
30/4 Arkansas
30/5 Brain

ACKNOWLEDGEMENTS

There are many people to thank for helping with the creation of the programme and this book that goes alongside it. Primarily, Bill Turnbull for taking on the project and so effortlessly transforming himself from broadcast journalist to quiz show host. Thanks also to the BBC for believing in the concept and allowing it to develop and grow, especially to Dan McGolpin and Jo Street for all their support and enthusiasm.

Thank you to those behind the scenes on the programme, who have worked so tirelessly in bringing the show to life, namely Chris Greenwood, Liz Gaskell, Claire Capaldi, Rob Dean and Derek Hallworth. And thank you to the executives Andy Culpin, Michael Mannes and Zoe Tait for leading the way.

Many thanks to Trevor Davies at Octopus and Shirley Patton at ITV for getting the book up and running. And without a lot of hard work by the question team, lead by Nick Pagan, in compiling the questions, there would be no book!

Finally, a huge part of the success of the show is down to the Think Tank itself. They answer hundreds of questions and spend hours under exam conditions to make sure the quiz plays fairly and squarely for the contestants. So to Abi Kanthabalan, Anisha Devadasan, Arminel Fennelly, Cleve Freckleton, Diane Hill, Jackie Waring, Jordan Humphries, Ken Fullicks, Len Crumbie, Lucy Barry, Mark Hogarth, Max Bruges, Peter Wong and Tristan Harper – congratulations and keep up the good work.

We really appreciate you buying this book, and hope that it will give you and your friends and family hours of fun and challenge you along the way. Good luck, and remember you can always bank on the Think Tank!

Octopus Publishing would like to thank the Think Tank production team and everyone at 12 Yard, ITV Studios and the BBC who helped in the creation of this book, especially Andy Culpin, Chris Greenwood, Michael Mannes, Shirley Patton and, of course, Bill Turnbull.

Additional text: Julian Flanders
Editorial Director: Trevor Davies
Editorial Assistant: Ellie Corbett
Designer: Jeremy Tilston
Senior Designer: Jaz Bahra
Assistant Production Manager: Marina Maher